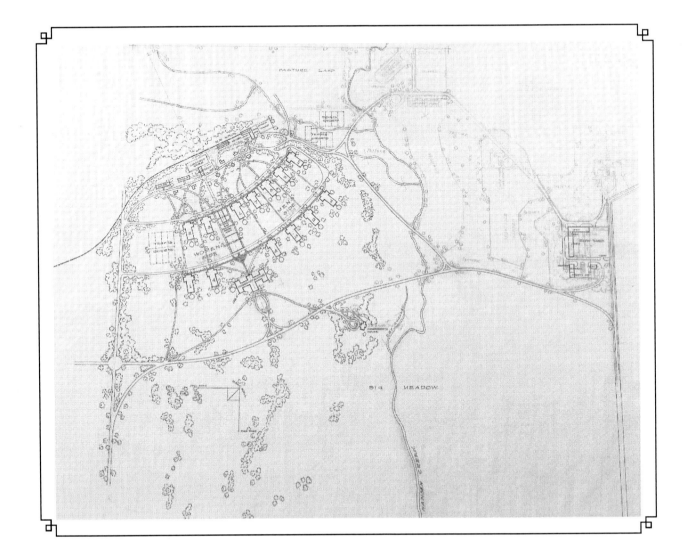

Under the Red Roof

One Hundred Years at Northern State Hospital

M. J. McGoffin

© 2011 by Mary J. McGoffin
ISBN Number: 978-0-692-01373-1
Library of Congress Control Number: 2011927870
Published by Mary J. McGoffin, Sedro-Woolley, WA
undertheredroofbook@gmail.com

ACKNOWLEDGMENTS

First order of gratitude goes to Kevin, Laura, Kathryn and Brendan who encouraged me to tell the hospital stories. Thank you to friends and family who read the early versions. The General Administration employees at the property offered helpful assistance. A special thanks to the people who contributed personal accounts of life at Northern State Hospital. Blanche V. Swalling, a student nurse in 1943, contributed the historic photos. A few of Ron Chamberlain's photos, from the National Registration of Historic Places' nomination, are included here.

About the Author

Mary Janicki McGoffin graduated from Sedro-Woolley High School in 1976. At Seattle University, she earned a Bachelor of Science degree in Nursing. She worked as an R.N. for United General Hospital and later for the school districts in Concrete and Sedro-Woolley.

PROLOGUE

December 28, 2006: Frosted fields shimmered in the winter sun. Hovering hills wore a blue mantle flecked with white snow. An absence of cars, trucks and trains gave way to a deep earthly silence. I had only to conquer my timidity. Usually I walked with a friend but today I came alone and, unwisely, defenseless: no whistle, no weapon and no dog. The Northern State Hospital cemetery lay just past the dairy barns on the outer fringes of the property, a fenced field with hundreds of patients interred, dating back to 1913. I thought it odd my breath froze in the air and ice crunched beneath my feet, yet the middle of the field remained soft. I approached for a closer look. Cold water seeped through my shoes and into my socks. Without grave markers, I stepped gingerly, not knowing exactly where the bodies lay. Across the ravine, I saw the hospital campus, a ghost of its former self. Mental illness didn't usually kill people, so I wondered, how did they die? One too many electric shock treatments? A lobotomy gone wrong? Suicide? Old age? Death by insanity?

Returning to the farm trail, I proceeded to wind my way through the pastures towards the hay barn on a knoll. Half way up the trail, I heard the howling and whining of voices across a wide swath of forest, ricocheting off Lyman Hill. I couldn't pinpoint where they were coming from but I knew I'd made a foolish mistake coming alone. Snarling, howling, ear piercing shrill sounds came rolling towards me as I quickly retreated, remembering if I ran, wild animals would give chase. At some point, I reasoned, the cries must be coyotes, a large pack of them. They surely saw me but I could not see them. What would I do anyway? Pick up a fallen-down fence post and start swinging it? Did the hawk tip them off? He had seen me come in.

During my childhood, I remember wailing, plaintive cries in the night, probably cats in heat or a pack of coyotes in the distance. I imagined they were the sounds of patients going mad. This much I knew: Northern State Hospital housed hundreds of patients only five miles away. They kept the violent ones in locked wards. Occasionally patients escaped. Some were never caught.

Forty years later, I realized how deeply the childhood association between the hospital and scary sounds had sunk into my subconscious. I found some rational answers. High-pitched animal cries sound unnervingly similar to wailing human voices. The cemetery is always wet because the surface water cannot penetrate the hardpan soil. Gravediggers weighed caskets down with rocks so the boxes wouldn't float. Coyotes do howl, though not usually midday. The property borders thousands of forest acres. Still, I took this as a warning to proceed carefully into the lives of patients past.

After walking the trails for a couple years and observing the red tiled roofs of the hospital buildings across Hansen Creek, I decided to approach the main entrance. "Closed campus" signs warned visitors to turn back. Over-grown ivy invaded the trees and vines strangled the abandoned guardhouse. I turned around and went home, deciding a phone call would be the prudent thing to do.

"Well, you'll need to talk to Dan Singleton," said Judy Holmes, the administrative assistant, in a business tone.

"I can make an appointment for you."

I imagined Judy to be three times bigger than she turned out to be. I pictured her like the gatekeeper in the Wizard of Oz checking me out through the hole in the door. As it turned out, Judy had been a drill sergeant and she still carried the bearing of one. I quickly learned how not to get my hair singed. During one of my early visits, she set the phone to the answering machine, stepped out the screen door, climbed on top of a weathered wooden picnic table and lit a cigarette.

"I've been here six years," she began.

"I tried to salvage as many things as I could before they tore the buildings down. Sometimes I pulled documents from the edges of burn piles."

Judy had a fiercely protective stance towards the hospital property and a soft heart for people she liked. In time, she let me into both of them.

On the day of my interview, I walked into the office and found Dan seated at the far side of a long conference table, baseball cap low over his eyes, arms folded across his big chest. I set aside my prepared questions. Dan needed little prompting. His stern, unshaven face and steady gaze never let up. The real work, the unsaid interview involved me being sized up for trustworthiness. He subtly surveyed my motives for snooping into the history of Northern State Hospital and not until we stumbled upon the common memory of my brother's sheep did the scrutiny begin to slacken. I came from a local family and that made me a local girl. He uncrossed his arms.

On June 24, 2009, Dan gave me office space to work in. Three months later, he died of complications from a heart attack. He regretted the demolition of buildings over the last two decades and vowed that no more would go down on his watch. None did.

Lyman Hill dominates the landscape above the haybarn and trails.
Photo: M.J. McGoffin, November 11, 2009

1

Sedro-Woolley, my hometown, began as a mining and logging hub. In 1909, local businessmen lobbied for the mental hospital and persuaded the governor's commission to purchase the initial 826 acres. In the ensuing one hundred years, the town and hospital grew up together. By the time another generation passes, all first hand experience of Northern State Hospital will be lost. From archival materials I gathered statistics on the hospital and from walking the land, pausing inside doorways and listening to the interviewees, I gathered the people's stories.

I lived in two worlds while working on the Northern State Hospital project. In my mind, I watched the bakers deliver birthday cakes to the wards. I smelled the strawberries in the cannery where women sat in the warm sun and hulled them for jam. I felt the heat of the greenhouse where women potted flowers. I felt their restlessness at night and heard the voices of the nurses down the hall. I sensed their loneliness in a sunroom crowded with patients. I heard the powerhouse whistle calling them to lunch—the clanging of metal plates, saucers and cups.

This is not the story the *Ghosthunter's* TV series tell in their "Lost Souls" episode on September 26, 2007. Richard Valentine directed and filmed two horror movies at the hospital, *Bloody Mary* (2006) and *The Taken* (2009), perpetuating the myth of the revengeful dead. If there are restless spirits, they deserve more respect than to be apprehended by a ghost-meter and camera glaring into empty rooms. If anything, they deserve a respectful, compassionate approach because of the trauma and suffering of their past lives.

2

The landscape architects hired to design the campus understood the spiritual dimensions of mental illness and sought to create a beautiful refuge for patients. The master plan consisted of exquisite hand drawings by John Charles Olmsted. Olmsted's father, Frederick, ended the last years of his life in McLean Hospital, near Boston, Massachusetts, a mental institution Frederick designed in 1895. When the younger Olmsted had a chance to design a mental institution on the west coast, he brought to the task personal experience of his father's mental illness.

The state of Washington gave Olmsted a remarkable setting to work with. He situated the hospital two miles east of Sedro-Woolley on a low bluff overlooking the Skagit Valley with views to the mountains. He considered every detail of the property, ensuring a seamless fit between the land and its use. The master plan of 1911 guided the hospital for fifty years.

In 1962, new roads cut into the wide expanses of lawn. Modern buildings signified a departure from the ward-style institution. New architecture required defacing the hospital's grand entrance. The suspended outdoor hallway looked like an intubation tube clumsily jammed down the throat of the venerable old hospital. Doctors used the surgery suite in the older building for a few years but the hundreds of rooms saw fewer and fewer patients. As life ebbed away from the institution, the long hallways and small rooms began to resemble a corpse, the structure intact but without the life-giving exchange of air and people.

Photo taken from Tyee Hill, looking southeast across the campus.
Photo: Blanche V. Swalling, 1943

Still, the beauty of the Olmsted landscape design endured. The plan, however, did not take into account the wild rampages Hansen Creek would take across the landscape. Only the local Indians knew what havoc the creek could cause.

Olmsted oriented the center of the campus on a southeast orientation for maximum light and mountain views. An imaginary straight line connects the rooftops.

Photo: M.J. McGoffin, September 11, 2009

Olmsted included the farm in the master design.
The white two-story farm annex has been demolished.
Photo: Blanche V. Swalling, 1943

3

The story of Northern State cannot be told without mentioning Hansen Creek. Before the advent of public water systems, an institution on the scale envisioned for Northern State required plentiful water on site. Hansen Creek drained an expansive watershed. I knew this to be true and personally never turned my back up-creek because of a looming premonition of how rapidly the waters could rise. Only someone who had studied the creek in all seasons could make any reasonable claim about predicting its behavior. The state engineers, on the other hand, imagined they could harness the creek's prodigious strength. They might as well have tried to bridle a stallion.

"There is every assurance," began the engineer in 1909, "that when cleared and cultivated the Northern Hospital farm will be the finest possessed by any of the state institutions." Within three years, the first superintendent understood why the Indians named Hansen Creek "The Big Smoky." Sudden snow-melts in the mountains turned the clear creek into a muddy rush of churning waters.

Years after the hospital closed, other agencies sought to return Hansen Creek to its original course. The chance to improve fish habitat became the rallying call to fund the project. In 2008, they installed a series of sediment dams strapped to pilings. The following winter, high waters tore the dams off their supports and pushed the tangled woody debris downstream. Undaunted, the agencies embarked on an extensive alluvial fan restoration. They gave Hansen Creek permission to sprawl on the condition that it gather itself together and exit the property under the only outlet available, a narrow passage beneath State Route 20. That the water did not cooperate exactly as planned came as no surprise to many observers of this wild creek.

The dairy barns and cannery can be seen in the distance on a low bluff, while the alluvial fan restoration project is shown in the foreground.
Photo: M.J. McGoffin, November 11, 2009

The untamable nature of this creek resembles the human spirit: it does not want to be restrained, ordered or manipulated. My respect for it is immense. Outsiders underestimated the raincloud's power to mold the landscape. The architects underestimated the rain's relentless wear on buildings.

4

I hold in my hand a cold, wet, broken piece of terra cotta tile imprinted with "DES MOINES CLAY CO., IOWA." The tile fragment broke loose from the roof of Ward E, one of four buildings constructed in 1917. Red clay tile connected the California missions like a bread-crumb trail through sunny southern California. To find it in the lichen-laden, fern-covered, deep-canopied forests of Western Washington seems like someone lost their way.

Architects specified Spanish Colonial Revival's signature material to roof the buildings at Northern State Hospital instead of cedar shakes, a locally sourced wood well adapted to the wet, verdant Skagit Valley. Cedar, the ubiquitous building material of Northwest Indians for thousands of years, was deemed not suitable.

When completed, the Spanish Colonial Revival style appeared over-dressed, a regal queen sitting among huge tree stumps and knee-deep mud. The State intended the over-the-top ornateness to soften the institutional character of the campus and they accomplished this magnificently. The architecture presented not only a contrast in color but also one of style: exquisite European refinement set in a corner of Washington Territory, a landscape just emerging from its first wave of pioneer settlements. The State intended the buildings to last one hundred years. They almost did. They could not have foreseen the social movements of the 1950's and 1960's that would derail their plans.

Maintaining the Spanish Colonial Revival style buildings proved to be a challenge even in the early days of the hospital. Green algae grew on the red clay tiles requiring the crews to douse the roofs with limewater. The acidity of fir needles, combined with long, rainy months, eroded away the copper valleys between roof lines, allowing water intrusions along the cracks. Upon closure of the hospital in 1973, the buildings had no watchman on duty and water crept, first through roofs, then down walls and finally into foundations.

One day, I met Steve Osier, carpenter and hospital historian, as he pulled his old pick-up truck along side me. Stray people on campus made him nervous. When the State tore down one of the wards, the crew saved the copper cupolas. Shortly thereafter, the heavy, ornamental copper disappeared. Steve took it upon himself to find the missing cache, valued at over $10,000. Meth addicts had tried to pawn the copper. Steve shared with me his determination to prevent any more buildings from being razed. Painstakingly, he replaced over 300 panes of small glass in Denny Hall in an effort to secure the building exterior. He took it upon himself to repair spalled stucco and re-paint with the original cream color. The inventory of hospital buildings encompassed over 600,000 square feet, an enormous amount of property to maintain, requiring the crew to triage their rescue efforts.

I remember the day Dan walked with me out to the southern fields and described how the crew filled the empty septic tanks with demolition debris. The remainder they pushed to the edge of the bluff and covered with dirt. No one would guess what lay beneath the wide meadow of grass, swaying in the wind. Terra cotta and ceramic tiles, maple wood floors, solid oak doors, polished wood handrails, ornate staircases, wood or steel divided light windows; materials once so carefully crafted and assembled now lay crunched into pieces, buried beneath the sod.

Today, in two of the abandoned buildings, wind rustles through broken windows, drafting down empty corridors. Blackberry vines slip through open panes and snake their way across tile floors and up walls of peeling paint. Brambles typically take over disturbed areas. Strange though, what attracts living leaves to an abandoned patient room bereft of sunlight, water and nutrients? Everything a plant needs to grow is outside this room. Apparently, one life has drained out of the place while a different life emerges. The decomposers, soil bacteria, are at work, pulling every brick, shingle, copper gutter and metal bracket back into the earth, recycling the man-made environment into its elemental forms again. Rain, a decomposer's best ally, hastens the process.

In an effort to preserve the story about Northern State Hospital, I submitted the property to the National Register of Historic Places. The National Park Service agreed the property made a significant contribution to our country's understanding of mental health care at the turn of the twentieth century. If a wider audience could hear the story, I thought, it might pique some interest in restoring the property's inherent beauty and giving it a new purpose. In January of 2011, the state government declared the property surplus and put it up for sale.

In 1916, the hospital added the Assembly Hall as a place to gather for social events.
Photo: M.J. McGoffin November 13, 2008

5

Dr. Doughty, the superintendent from approximately 1913-1949, scrupulously accounted for every dollar entrusted to him. Dealing with the contractors during the build-out phase of the campus required him to follow up on the nuts and bolts of construction and to hold his ground with suppliers over the price of goods. In addition, he provided medical care to the patients and leadership for his staff. An immensely meticulous man, Dr. Doughty's volumes of correspondence at the state archive office filled several huge boxes. In great detail, he described the emergence of the site from a primitive farm operation to a first class mental institution. He responded to requests for employment or letters from detective agencies such as the one looking for a young lawyer from the east coast who fell into drinking in Seattle. Northern State Hospital became his kingdom. Every two years, he wrote to his superiors, like an explorer in a foreign land.

Dr. Doughty maintained the hospital through two world wars. Employees left to enlist, exacerbating his staffing problems in the wards. The wave of immigrants who flooded the United States also found their way to his hospital. He attempted to deport the "undesirables" but was hampered by the Immigration Laws and the presence of submarines still roaming the oceans.

Dr. Doughty's empire comprised an ever-growing population of patients. He discharged very few and he certainly had his bias of which ones to keep. In addition to foreigners, he had no sympathy for drug addicts. Admissions could be voluntary, by court commitment, an emergency, for temporary care or for observation. Each biennium, Dr. Doughty noted the patients paroled or escaped, deported and repatriated, transferred from other hospitals or discharged—jailor terms used to describe the mentally ill. Northern State Hospital never fenced in their property and patients wandered into the countryside and were found sleeping in barns or knocking on farmhouse doors, according to Robert Harrison, a local resident. The criminally insane constituted a very small number of the patient population and were housed in a locked down ward on the farthest edge of the campus.

In 1926, the hospital numbered seven hundred forty-three white men, five hundred twenty-four white women, nine colored men and eleven colored women. Causes for admission included insanity, epilepsy, mental defects, alcoholism, drug addiction, and neurosyphilism, among other cases. A patient diagnosed insane and epileptic, "... should be counted as insane."

This statistic I found particularly devastating. My brother developed epilepsy at age five. No one would have considered him insane; however, without the control achieved by anti-convulsant drugs, he might have been. In another era, my brother would have been a patient at Northern State Hospital without the love of his parents and the companionship of his brothers and sisters, a difficult scenario to imagine.

At Northern State Hospital, many of the patients contributed to the hospital community through some kind of useful work. In 1926, two-thirds of the patient population, over eight hundred men and women, worked in various jobs around the hospital. I found a document describing the one hundred and one patients who arrived by train in the hospital's first year.

In the early years, the doctors lived in the Administration building. Dr. Doughty's office would have been here.
Photo: Blanche V. Swalling, 1943

In 1938, a receiving ward was added to the north entrance of the Administration building.
Photo: Blanche V. Swalling, 1943

In 1923, Dr. Doughty built the gate-house and new entrance across the ravine. Note the physician cottages on the hill to the right, built in 1935. They are no longer standing.
Photo: Blanche V. Swalling, 1943

Dr. Doughty constructed an earthen dam with a culvert in the ravine which created ponds on either side of the road. The ponds drain into Brickyard creek and eventually into the Skagit River. Today, the Steel-head Club hosts a children's fishing event here each spring.
Photo: Blanche V. Swalling, 1943

The boiler house, constructed around 1928, heated water for the cannery. The roothouses built in the early 1920's stored winter vegetables. This photo was taken from the bridge across Hansen Creek.
Photo: Blanche V. Swalling, 1943

The Olmsted plan placed grazing pastures in the distance and more labor-intensive activities, such as orchards and gardening, closer to the wards.
Photo: Blanche V. Swalling, 1943

6

Dr. McLeish, the first superintendent, filed his biennial report in 1910-1912 and tallied data in rows and columns, reducing the lives of patients to statistics. Who were these men? In my mind's eye, I saw them standing silently before me. The gulf of years dissolved between us.

In 1911, the state allotted seventy-five cents per day for each patient's care. The majority of the patients were between twenty-five and fifty years of age and had lived at Fort Steilacoom for several years, a converted military outpost near Tacoma, Washington. Together they represented a wide swath of occupations. Counted among their ranks were a barber, a blacksmith, a boiler-maker, a butcher, carpenters, cooks, engineers, farmers, firemen, a fisherman, a gardener, an ironmoulder, laborers, longshoremen, loggers, miners, painters, paperhangers, sailors, a salesman, a sawyer, a shingle-weaver, tailors, a teamster and an upholsterer. Some of them left behind wives, though most were single and foreigners in a new land: their citizenry represented Austria, Canada, Denmark, England, Ecuador, France, Finland, Germany, Ireland, Italy, Norway, Nova Scotia, Poland, Portugal, Russia, Scotland, Sweden, Switzerland. How they found their way to our shores was not given. Thirty-six of them claimed United States citizenship.

The causes of their mental disease varied. According to the categories of the day, confinement to a mental institution could have been due to: alcohol, congenital reasons, exposure, financial trouble, hereditary causes, injury to head, isolation, love affair, masturbation, morphine, religion, starvation, sunstroke, syphilis or worry. An "unknown reason" accounted for one out of every two admissions. An unknown reason triggered aberrant behavior and thoughts, so much so that their family, or the law, involuntarily committed them to an insane asylum in the Pacific Northwest.

The medical lexicon of the day described their diagnosis in these terms: psychoses from exhaustion or intoxication, organic dementia such as Huntington's Chorea, cerebral syphilis, cerebral trauma, melancholia or delusional insanity. Forty-four had maniac-depressive insanity, seven exhibited paranoia, one had epileptic insanity and four were imbeciles.

In the early years, Northern State Farm gave them a place to heal and a purpose: to grow food and send it to the patients at Fort Steilacoom who had abysmal soil to work with. Before long, the institution's name changed to Northern State Asylum: "asylum" from the Greek word asulon or sanctuary.

In 1912, Northern State Asylum discharged three patients who recovered. Three tried to escape but were returned. Five escaped successfully. Before the year was over, six were dead. The cause? Dementia and exhaustion, epilepsy, general paresis or pulmonary tuberculosis. The 1912 biennium report didn't mention the one killed by a falling barn in the windstorm. A fellow patient by the name of Eric, however, remembered the day and hour it happened. I came across Eric's story chronicling the early days of the hospital. A local journalist by the name of Dick Fallis re-printed the hospital newsletters from 1936 including Eric's series of articles. I was less interested in the minutiae of the whole year but intensely interested in the first person account given by Eric.

7

To find a patient to interview proved to be a challenge. Fortunately, Eric's writing offered a patient's perspective. I have compiled and edited his story for clarity:

My parents raised a large family on a farm near the seashore. I went to school during the winter and helped on the farm the rest of the year. I was of average intelligence for that community; a strong, muscular type of young man with a yearning for experiences my home surroundings could not furnish. Young men shipped out on vessels in trade or fishing from the seaport near my home. I yearned for an ocean voyage to some foreign port. Many of my friends settled in the timber belt of the United States. I had little difficulty in finding plenty of hard work in the woods. The crews of these camps, a hardy, reckless group, drank and gambled often and I drifted into the ways of the average logger. I prided myself on the experiences, but in due time, I found I overestimated my strength and ability.

I drifted about until I found myself dependent and in a State hospital. Being unable to understand my condition, I resented being confined, rebelled and caused no end of trouble. I wanted to be out in the open where I could breathe the fresh air and build up my body and mind. This opportunity came to me in 1910 when Washington State transferred patients from Steilacoom to clear land for a new hospital site. I gladly joined up with a small company of men. Few of you here, enjoying the luxuries of this hospital, have any concept of the conditions as I first saw them.

The train stopped near the old Tyler house on Hansen Creek. We constructed a frame building to serve as temporary living quarters. Unfortunately, a very severe storm struck on New Year's night, 1910, and this building collapsed about 10:30 p.m., killing one man. The gale reportedly reached seventy miles per hour and the temperature hovered near zero. All were suddenly thrown out into the night, half clothed, no place to go except the sheds, chicken houses and the Tyler house.

In the early days, Hansen Creek was so small I could jump across it. As logging of the hills began, frequent rampages by the creek occurred, seemingly in protest against these agencies. The first severe flood I remember occurred in 1915. The creek rose rapidly due to a Chinook wind and washed away the bank causing the dairy barn to collapse and fall into the water. All bridges to the farm were washed out leaving us without access to the hospital buildings.

In time, we moved into a well-heated, fireproof building close to the farm, but with all that some of the boys pined for the old wooden ward. The one hundred men living there enjoyed all the liberties possible in an institution. It seemed more like a club; the boys enjoying playing games, smoking, reading, pool, radio, all free to go as they pleased in the evenings. Reliable watchmen supervised the men and never locked them in but cared for any emergencies which might arise. It was in fact a fine comfortable home.

I was transferred to the building crew, clearing the site for the Administration building under the supervision of a young inspector by the name of Warbuck. With the building about half finished, the administrators planned a dedication. I could never figure out why they were in such a hurry unless they feared an election might deprive them of the opportunity. Great crowds came from the country in wagons and by horseback. I saw some of the visitors strolling about the covered walks, arm in arm in a merry mood, such as you might expect to see at a county fair or circus.

Patients continued to arrive by train from Steilacoom. Women patients came to provide housekeeping and work in the laundry while the men worked the farm. One of the new men shouted about me, "What is that scab doing here? Why did they send us up here with that wop?" To get out of his way, I asked for something else to do and went to work in the kitchen with Mr. Johnson, the boss cook.

I remember a patient named McLain who had worked as a Canadian lumberjack. He was a powerful man, very religious, excitable and sometimes disturbed, especially when kept indoors. The hospital staff thought it necessary to keep him in restraints to prevent injury to himself or others. I remember the day Dr. Doughty came on the ward and saw him strapped to a bench.

The doctor said, "Hello Jim. What are you doing here?"

Jim said, "They have me hogtied here all day on this bench and I want to get out and go to work. Any man would go stark mad to have to sit here tied all day." The doctor called the attendant aside and had a talk with him. To our surprise, he gave Jim an axe the next day, promoted him to straw boss of the crew and sent him to clear the entrance of the grounds from the gate to the county road. I wish some of you could have seen that man engineer the job. He had a giant's strength. He died several years ago while falling a tree.

During the construction of the ward buildings, I met Scotty. It took a strong man to follow Scotty, a great worker. Later, the hospital gave him charge of the horses. In time he became our farm boss. Patients like myself did most of the work building the concrete barns and we did an excellent job if I do say it.

Some days and weeks have passed since I promised to write, but I have had a fine cold. I enjoyed a good excuse for taking a resting spell except the annoyance of some of the fellows here. They talk about things I write, saying I don't tell it right. I hear it most of the day and of late they hurl echoes and vibrations at me during the night to keep me awake. If I get to sleep, they send radio and electric waves and currents through the springs of my bed to shock my system. I located the responsible parties and they are wise to it for fear I will report them. They have eased up and they might as well, as I am going to write about these barns anyway, whether they are interested or not.

I will have to close now, as the gang is getting busy shooting flashlights about my room and turning the rays on me. I wish I had the whole bunch out on the Grand Banks in a fisherman's dory off a fore-and-aft fishing schooner, I would keep them too busy to annoy me and be away from their infernal machines.

In 1923, hospital employees and patients began replacing the wood barns, built in 1915, with concrete ones. The farm operation continued to expand until the 1950s.

Photo: M.J. McGoffin, March 5, 2008

8

With Eric, we see the hospital through the activities of men. Women patients engaged in more domestic work. I discovered the sewing room report for December of 1928 among Dr. Doughty's files. What kind of place made fifteen hundred Christmas candy bags for the patients? Every article of clothing and linen came from industrious hands. Items sewn conveyed a certain refinement: aprons, pillow shams, dresses, doilies, princess slips, vests and centerpieces. In photos of the dining hall, folded cloth napkins sit at each setting. In one month, the hospital made seventy-nine pairs of sheets, ninety-six overalls, fifty-four jackets, thirty-six shirts and three hundred towels, plus bibs, bloomers, brassieres and straight jackets.

The seamstresses mended as well. In just one month they repaired five blankets, forty-six bedspreads, four bags, three mangle pads, thirty-eight overalls, twenty-seven jumper jackets, eighty-two undergarments, forty shirts, eighteen pillowcases, eight trousers, ten coats and eighteen camisoles. I like to think the women patients found this work therapeutic and enjoyable. They could visit together. Many of them most likely brought sewing skills from home where they learned the craft from their mothers and grandmothers. Did they look forward to getting out of bed and hurrying to the sewing room to finish their projects? Certainly theirs was purposeful work.

9

I tried to imagine the life of the nurses, for the most part women, who lived and worked at Northern State Hospital. Dr. Doughty presided over the smallest details of these young women's lives. He wrote the following rules for the nurses' quarters:

- Keep room clean and orderly.
- Only fruit allowed in room.
- No cooking.
- Lights out at 10:30 p.m.
- Don't use patients to clean your room.
- No men allowed under any circumstances.

The entire building, he reminded the nurses, was under the direction and inspection of the housekeepers who reported any violations. Any obvious disregard for the rules was sufficient cause for immediate dismissal. This seemed harsh to me; expelled because of eating something besides fruit in your room?! Just when I imagined the lives of these spirited young women being hemmed-in by an overbearing superintendent, I learned from some of them, now in their eighties, of antics they participated in. After hours, the gate swung shut across the road and locked them in for the night. The railroad spur, behind the nurses' quarters, however, provided a clear path to the county road. The nurse supervisor told me how she drove her car down the tracks at night. On weekends, one nurse described how they snuck out at dark to go the Seven Cedars dancehall in Mt. Vernon. She showed me a photo of her and her roommate smoking cigarettes while sitting on their beds.

The railroad spur came into the campus behind Trevennen Hall, near the telephone pole in the photograph.

Photo: Blanche V. Swalling, 1943

Nurses' quarters also known as Trevennen Hall, built in 1938, continued the Spanish-Colonial Revival architecture theme.

Photo: M.J. McGoffin, November 11, 2009

While men were not allowed in the nurses' quarters, the young nurses and male attendants found ways to meet. A young attendant named Melrose regularly gave "tours" of the tunnels underground between buildings. The young nurses were not to be denied their social outlets. In a place as difficult as a mental institution where the nurses lived on campus with patients in nearby wards, it seems escaping for a few hours to the city provided a much needed return to the outside world.

10

Psychiatric nursing emerged as a specialty in its own right. I interviewed several nurses who made a career of working at Northern State Hospital. I met Gloria Lausch, one of the nurse supervisors, at her home on Big Lake.

"I fell in love working with the psyche patients," began Gloria. "One patient in particular had the rarest pure paranoia. We wrote back and forth until he died."

Together with Nancy Kintner, she helped pioneer the profession of psychiatric nursing at Northern State Hospital. The hospital provided a six-month internship for nurses.

"That way we weeded out the bad ones," she said.

"In the 1960s, patients came in with all kinds of drugs on board and we used a machine with electrical stimulation to help drain the drugs out of the body. We kept the violent women patients in wards L and M. The attic above housed the classrooms for nurses."

Gloria said the retired nurses now met once a month for lunch, and she arranged for "her girls" to meet me for a luncheon at one of the former physician apartments. Even after all these years, the women accorded Gloria the respect of a nurse supervisor.

Several months later, I contacted Joanne {Griffith} McInnes at her home in Sedro-Woolley to follow up on an interview:

> In the early 1950's, hospitals, in general, gave inexperienced student nurses too much responsibility. I did not feel this way at NSH, however, because the administration placed a high priority on education. As I drove onto the grounds of NSH to start my three-month rotation in "psych" nursing, I remember the feeling of fear and quickly locked my car doors. This fear did not last, thankfully, due to an excellent University of Washington nursing professor who taught and supervised our clinical experiences. I decided to work in this field of nursing. After graduation, I began my career in women's admissions.
>
> In hindsight, I feel we grasped for ways to treat and relieve patients' suffering. For example, we used the Funkenstein test to diagnose mania-depressive illness. We gave a medication to the patients and then recorded the observations over a specific time period and graphed their blood pressure and pulse.
>
> We gave a treatment called "peripheral stimulation" to some patients.

The staff attached moist saline pads to the back of patient's legs and arms. The patient received a low voltage of electricity that caused twitching, not grand mal seizures.

In addition, the hospital used Electro-Convulsive Therapy (ECT) and Insulin Coma Therapy. Gradually, the physicians introduced new medications such as Thorazine. We used leather and canvas restraints, as well as sedating medications, to control behavior.

Some patients received ECT two to three times a week. Patients with a diagnosis of depression seemed to benefit the most, in my memory and humble opinion. A physician administered the procedure with the patient lying on his/her bed. The R.N. applied the electrodes to their temples, placed a mouthpiece, and held their jaw to prevent injury. One to four staff held the patient's limbs to protect the joints and bones. That was then. Improvement evolved. Later, we gave patients a quick-acting anesthetic intravenously and supplemental oxygen. Following the treatment, we turned the patients on their side and they went into a brief, but deep sleep. As they recovered, the patients looked much calmer.

Dr. Jones, the superintendent, administered Insulin Coma Therapy and I was transferred to work there. Generally, patients receiving this daily treatment were cooperative. Usually they had a diagnosis of schizophrenia. In the morning, we put the patients to bed in a large dorm room. We gave large doses of insulin, according to orders. The patients went through various stages of sleep and we documented the results such as pupil size and vital signs. Usually they perspired profusely. Dr. Jones would tell us when to "bring them out" which meant administer I.V. glucose. I do remember one patient died of an irreversible coma.

As I reminisce, I wonder if the real treatment for these patients was the special attention they received. They ate special food and engaged in social activities that promoted a definite feeling of belonging. Kitty, a staff member, not a nurse but a matronly woman with a constant smile, doted on them like a mother.

I worked on the men's medical/surgical ward in the mid-1950's. One Saturday, I remember in particular because Dr. Jones invited Dr. Walter Freeman, a psychiatrist from the East coast and noted author at the time, to perform two lobotomies. Dr. Freeman took over the surgery room in an authoritarian manner. Our nurses' training taught us to stand when a doctor entered and always show respect. If we were using the only chair available, we were expected to give it up for the doctor.

The patients treated with lobotomies often were burdened with aggressive behavior and did not respond to other treatments. Before the lobotomy, we gave the patient ECT as part of an anesthetic. For most patients, a lobotomy subdued aggressive behavior. One patient I remember had a fantastic memory. Following the procedure, he did not seem to lose his personality or ability to function. He remained friendly and had some freedom of the campus. After the hospital closed, I heard he had moved to Seattle and lived in the community.

I also worked on admissions for geriatric women patients. Dr. Fred Darvill, the ward doctor, was interested in research and made arrangements with pharmaceutical companies for drug studies. I remember observing and documenting the results for drugs like Ritalin and Cytomel.

Today I feel as though I'm still in "psych nursing" even though I retired

in 1988. My husband suffers from vascular dementia. I cared for him prior
to his admission to Birchview Memory Care Center.

*Student nurse, Anna Pennell, lived at
Trevennen Hall in 1943.*
Photo: courtesy of the Alderwood Manor
Heritage Association

11

The psychiatric profession searched for the locus of mental disease. If a physical defect could be located then treatment would focus on a physical cure. Even though doctors couldn't find anything structurally abnormal on autopsy, they persisted in pursuing physical treatments.

In 1936, a Portuguese neurologist, Dr. Egas Moniz discovered he could rid one-third of patient's symptoms by small corings in the frontal lobe in a surgery called a prefrontal leucotomy. He based his experiment on the observation that people with frontal lobe injuries tended to be calmer and less prone to depression. In 1949, he won the Nobel Prize in medicine for this procedure.

In 1946, James Watts, a neurosurgeon experimented with cutting the nerves to the thalamus in an effort to cut off the brain's connection to its emotional center. Patients relapsed in three to four months and underwent a second and sometimes third surgery. In time, Dr. Watts began performing the surgery on conscious patients in order to refine the process. The patient's agitation subsided and the process prevented the descent into madness but the patient became demobilized and apathetic.

Walter Freeman, a neurologist, not a surgeon and therefore not licensed to enter the brain surgically, teamed up with Dr. Watts. Together they sought a way to more completely ablate the white matter tracts to and from the prefrontal lobes. The procedure came to be known as the transorbital lobotomy since it required entering the frontal lobe through the eye socket and scraping away tissue with a sharp instrument like a windshield wiper across a window. Mental conflicts no longer distressed the patients but they had little capacity for any emotional experience. Dr. Freeman courted the newspapers and touted his procedure as a miracle surgery. The medical profession considered public criticism of another professional unethical and therefore Dr. Freeman's claims went unchallenged.

Psychosurgery became popular in the 1940's. The number of chronically institutionalized patients soared during and after World War II, overwhelming the capacity of hospitals. Lobotomies provided a way to discharge patients back to their homes. By August 1949, nearly 10,000 operations had been performed in the United States.

The Nazi atrocities during World War II shocked the American public, and exposure of similar inhuman conditions in mental hospitals spurred the demand to do something for the patients. Freeman offered a simplified lobotomy to be done on a conscious patient without anesthetic or patient consent. Hospitals discharged these treated patients because they were no longer violent or agitated. They sent delusional patients to the wards for untreatable cases. The number of lobotomies decreased markedly with the development of narcoleptics, starting with chlorpromazine in 1952. In 1967, a patient died as Dr. Freeman performed a lobotomy and the medical profession stripped him of his privileges.

Curiosity about lobotomies continues to this day, especially by a generation with no familiarity of them. *The American Experience: The Lobotomist* on PBS Home Video received over 300,000 views on YouTube by June of 2010.

12

I found a copy of the matron's report dated 1939 for one of the women's wards and I began to see why the cemetery was so full. The matron described medical emergencies such as a fever of 105 degrees with the same brevity and even tone as the patient throwing clothes out the window. Chaos seemed barely contained.

Description of patients (names withheld) and treatments:

- Destructive, noisy, incontinent, fighting and kicking nurses. Put in "camisole" (a soft fabric restraint). Slept well all night.
- Using abusive language, assaultive. Put in camisole, secluded. Sodium Amytal Gr. 6 given at 11.15 a.m. Taken out of camisole at 12 noon. Quiet afternoon.
- Adrenalin 1 cc for abdominal distention during night, relieved.
- Escaped from kitchen when food was being let in. Brought back to ward by nurse.
- Very severe grand mal seizures @ 9:30 p.m., 11 p.m., 4 a.m., 5:45 a.m.
- Temp 105 degrees. Alcohol sponge bath and cold pack to spine. Finger nails cyanotic, mask-like expression to face.
- Resistive, threw clothes out of the window.
- Spinal puncture by Dr. Shelton.
- Irritable and sarcastic. Stuporous, apathetic.
- Haughty and demanding. Uncooperative about taking medications.
- Very restless and talkative until 1 a.m. Asked to be put in camisole. Quieter but did not sleep.

- Sodium Phenobarbital 2 cc. I.M. (intramuscular) at 12 midnight, effective.
- Laughing, talking, singing at intervals until 3 a.m.
- Complained of "cold." Given warm olive oil in ears.
- Seven teeth extracted.
- Sharp pain in chest. Dr. ordered enema given with good results.
- Threw dishes in dining room at breakfast time. Put in camisole and secluded.

In the administration building, the surgery suites, treatment rooms and offices were in the central hall while men and women wards comprised the wings. This is the hospital's women's ward.

Photo: M.J. McGoffin, November 8, 2008

- Broke out two windowpanes inside room. Put in cuffs and belt. Sodium Amytal Gr. 6 given at 11:45 p.m. Effective.

It does not take a large leap of imagination to picture this scene. Imagine the scene multiplied by twenty-seven wards.

The 1912 hospital building included outdoor fire escape chutes from the second story.
Photo: M.J. McGoffin, November 11, 2009

13

None of my interviewees could claim thirty-two years of history with Northern State Hospital except Barbara Ward-Thompson. We sat at her kitchen table with flower cuttings nearby on the windowsill; family photos layered on the refrigerator and stacks of papers half read. A well-worn tea kettle simmered in the background. I e-mailed her the questions beforehand and she prepared for the interview with the thoroughness of a college assignment. Toward the end of our time together, she brought from her attic a cardboard box full of newspaper clippings, articles written by doctors, obituaries and miscellaneous papers, a goldmine of information. In Barbara's words:

In 1939, Dr. Newkirk fled Europe and, after a brief time on the east coast, he came to work at Northern State Hospital as a psychiatrist. His daughter Laurie became my lifetime friend. We met in 1941, as sophomores in high school. I watched the daily life of patients as they moved about the hospital grounds. I watched how the patients brought groceries into the doctor's house. The doctors dictated these massive histories and massive psychiatric exams to be transcribed. While still in high school, Laurie and I worked as transcriptionists.

Northern State Hospital had a nursing training program out there for years and Dr. Newkirk taught in this program. Gals would come from Bellingham, Everett and Seattle for their psychiatric rotation. Today, every now and then you will hear a nurse say with pride and fond memories that she worked out there. The hospital hired my brother John, a high school student to be a night watchman. He took his Irish setter for company. At night in those early days without streetlights, the campus was spooky.

In the early days, they used hydrotherapy, basically water baths, maybe they even used cold water, I'm not sure. They wrapped the patients in canvas restraints to keep them from hurting themselves. It was terrible.

I left Sedro-Woolley to major in chemistry at college. After my first year, the hospital hired me the following summer to be a lab technician. I had a lab window that looked out on the courtyard. I could see patients pacing and pacing; it was like a prison that way. The Denny building had a courtyard on the men's side and one on the women's side.

I guess they did a few lobotomies up there but it wasn't any lobotomy mill. The aberrant behavior would be brought under control but then you had this zombie. The patient was like an infant again and would have to learn how to crawl, walk, and feed himself.

Frequently I saw the better patients in the corridors. In the old, old days, in order to keep the patients busy, the patients polished the terrazzo floors. A phalanx of patients, with carpet tacked to blocks, swept back and forth keeping the terrazzo floors shiny. Not a few people broke their hips falling on those slippery floors.

I wonder whether the morgue is still there. A lot of patients simply died of old age and from sicknesses like pneumonia. Occasionally someone committed suicide and would be found hanging outside from an orchard tree. I think they used local morticians. If there were family, the hospital turned the body over to them. If not, the hospital had a little cemetery on the outskirts of the farm. They would have Sunday church services in the chapel, along with movies and dances. Local ministers rotated up there and gave services.

When Charlie Jones came in 1949, the changes began. In the 1950's, they dismantled the farm. It became unprofitable to maintain the herds. The hospital canned a lot of meat and applesauce. The farm, greenhouse, sawmill and power plant kept many patients busy. Some patients worked in the office, on the switchboard or performing clerical work. I don't think the use of patients was seen as slave labor but as part of the treatment program. I didn't hear any criticism. Laundry went out dirty and came back clean. They felt they were contributing and had a sense of self worth. Patients delivered live plants from the greenhouses to the wards where they immediately died because it was so hot.

Dr. Jones hired Saul Spiro to set up the resident training program in the 1950's and he ran it for years. Saul invited me and the other social workers to take part and learn about the philosophy of community psychiatry.

On the acute units, patients would come in, get treated and go home. They could come back and we would do the same thing all over again. My philosophy was not so much that these people ever got well but they had a illness they had to learn to control if they were going to make it outside. Did many come back? Oh yes, heavens yes, because there wasn't the support outside for them. A few wards housed people who didn't seem to get better.

The ones most gratifying to treat were the depressed because depression was treatable. In the early days they did a lot of shock treatment. They tapered off the intensity to maintenance levels of shock treatments. After a treatment, the patient acted like someone who had a seizure. As the doctors became more sophisticated, they learned to sedate the patient before they gave them the electric shock, then it wasn't so hard on the patients.

The diagnosis called schizo-affective had a bipolar component. We could treat the bipolar symptoms but couldn't cure the underlying psychosis; therefore, they would only get half better. Patients with personality disorders came in but we didn't very often cure those. Alcoholic drug psychosis began to happen in the 1960's. The intensive units admitted psychotics wigged out on street drugs. They had to be detoxed first, then you didn't know what kind of personality you would find underneath. We never knew if they were experiencing psychotic symptoms first and trying to treat themselves with alcohol and psychedelic meds or did they dabble in the meds first and precipitate a psychosis. They were terrible to deal with.

Menopausal depression responded to treatment for the most part. Doctors discharged women on prescriptions and we set them up with aftercare. Some were profoundly depressed. If the depression wouldn't budge with meds, they were prime candidates for ECT. The depression cleared up. It was just a miracle. It always aggravated me when people saw ECT as torture because for profound depression it was the treatment of choice. Sometimes it would be a permanent improvement. Sometimes they would need another treatment.

The whole world it seemed derided Sedro-Woolley as the town that had the bughouse. The hospital was self-contained and didn't need to reach out to the town for much, maybe for the postal service. Still, people equated the town with the mental hospital. Many deaths were associated with the closing of Northern State Hospital; patients who couldn't stand the change, staff who could not stand the change. Many, many people got depressed. It was profound.

The door and ramp on the right provided access to the enclosed courtyard.
Photo: M.J. McGoffin, July 15, 2008

14

In a small town like Sedro-Woolley, where Barbara shares a garden patch with my brother Mike, one tip leads to another. My sister's mother-in-law suggested I interview her neighbor, Sally Hinds. When I arrived, Sally slowly unlatched the door lock, let me in, and then turned to sit down at a small table. I noticed the boxes of junior mints stacked in a pile, the Smith-Corona typewriter, a TV Guide, ashtray, magnifying lens, box of Kleenex, portable radio, allergy sinus medicine and bag of open chips. She lived in a space smaller than a rescue boat at sea. I arrived with a few winter squash and offered to cut them in half for her.

"Oh no," she waved me off, "George, he left me sharp knives."

And I realize she didn't live to be eighty-eight years old by letting other people cut her squash. No doubt this elderly, bent woman, looking at me like nobody's fool, could wield a cleaver just fine.

"I know your mother," Sally said. "She gets her hair done at the same place I do."

This connection afforded me admittance into her world. She began:

In late 1944, about this time of the year, I came out here from Minnesota to work for Boeing. I didn't like the setup though. Since I paid my own way out here, I didn't have to stay with the company. If they paid your expenses you had to stay until that debt was paid off. I could just tell them to "kiss off." We had to pay rent on cramped living quarters—they charged for everything, it seems including the coffee cups. I had worked for Ma Bell in Minnesota and could go back to the telephone company. I didn't want to stay in Seattle.

I knew George and decided to come up here. Some of his relatives had come from Minnesota too. We married in 1945. My brother-in-law worked as a doctor at Northern State. They needed someone in the accounting office and since I had taken accounting all those years in high school, I applied for the job. I only worked one month before the male superintendent came in and said,

"Pack up your stuff. You'll be my secretary."

"I don't take shorthand," I tried to explain.

"You don't have to," he commanded.

I wondered what kind of secretary job he had in mind.

A job opened up at the switchboard and I moved to that position. We talked to people in the hall through a window. When I first started, all new patients came through the switchboard/reception area.

In 1955 the hospital sent travel guards to Seattle to pick up patients once a week. Sometimes family members or police brought patients in. One night, a policeman brought in a patient covered in blood. He wasn't hurt so I figured the blood had to come from someone else. Another time, a fellow brought his wife in. His papers said to take her to Eastern State, near Spokane, but he wanted her closer to home. We arranged her papers so she could stay, and her husband visited frequently. On visiting day, people signed in and out at the reception desk. The hospital put some patients on terminal leave or let them out to their families for a week, two weeks or a month. Some patients the hospital released completely.

We kept the keys. We handed them out to incoming people who had okays to pick them up. Certain employees picked up keys on a daily basis like Rosie Wilson, R.N. who picked up keys to the surgery department. The switchboard operator kept the key to the drug room. My first day on the 3-11 shift, Dr. Jones came in wearing gardening clothes from working outside, and asked for the drug room keys.

I said, "I'm sorry I can't give you any keys if I don't have proof of who you are."

He was the superintendent but I didn't know that. He stomped out. The next day, Dr. Geoff called me into her office and climbed all over my frame about it. I defended myself right then and there and said,

"Would you give keys to just anyone without I.D.?"

They backed off after that. We had good doctors even though some were foreign.

We notified the male supervisor or female supervisor when something came up and called the doctor on duty. One patient came in alone at night, asking to see Dr. Newkirk and I didn't know if I should be scared or not. Why they gave him a week of terminal leave I had no idea. He had tried to kill a doctor.

"I thought you were on terminal leave?" I asked and then I noticed he didn't have any shoes on. He could see I was getting a nervous.

"I wouldn't touch you. Your husband works at the powerhouse."

This patient knew karate and had every bartender in town under his thumb. He created havoc in town but one night he picked the wrong bar. My husband bartended part-time and the patient had made a judo pass at

George. My husband, a champion wrestler and ex-navy man, learned karate and judo when stationed in the Orient and surprised the patient with swift counter-moves. That patient picked with the wrong man. George threw him out of the bar. It wasn't until I got home that I learned George had worked him over.

I had Monday and Tuesdays off. My husband had Sundays and Mondays off so we had one day together. My husband knew one of the cooks. He ordered steaks and the kitchen delivered them to George at the powerhouse. Sometimes the kitchen brought me a meal if I was working alone since I couldn't leave the switchboard unattended. The food came on metal trays: a dinner plate, a cup of coffee and dessert, a regular meal.

I liked the work even though a few things did happen I didn't like. Patients had to go to court before they came to us. One man they picked up off the street somewhere had to be washed with a scrub brush to get him cleaned.

Early one evening, after dinner, I remember a patient who climbed onto the second floor of the administration building staircase and threatened to jump over the railing. She would have jumped, but they grabbed her in time. One man had his hands up over his head all they time, like he was waving things away. He thought something was falling on his head. Someone got the idea to buy him a hat and he stopped doing it. I remember a patient, a colored man, came every day with a full #2 coffee can of wild blackberries and sold them for $3.00. That was dang cheap for wild blackberries.

About six months or longer before I left, the hospital installed a new switchboard. The switchboard had a key like a toggle switch. If you flipped the switch you could hear the conversation. When we recorded a conversation, we had to stay on the line. The recording machine looked like a record player. The machine sat next to us and we were in charge of it. We labeled the record and then another department filed it in the patient's history.

We recorded telephone conversations with families about the death of a patient. One time, in particular, I remember a patient had passed away. Dr. Timeroff called the number for next of kin in the patient's file. A woman in Seattle answered. When we told her the news we heard nothing. The doctor tried to talk to her. We didn't know whether she had passed out or had a heart attack or what. There was no one else to notify. We contacted the police to go to her address and make sure she was all right. She evidently just couldn't talk.

We had a mortuary and held patient bodies for a certain period of time. If they couldn't find a family member or someone to claim them the hospital staff buried them in the cemetery. The hospital cremated some of them. Somebody out there in Olympia in the 1960's made a ruling the patients couldn't work on the farm. I don't know how many patients came to the switchboard and wanted to know why they couldn't work. They didn't want to fiddle their hands all day. That was ridiculous.

"Veto" Evans {Governor Dan Evans}, that's what we called him, had something to do with that. He swore he was going to close the hospital because no one voted for him and he did. I think closing the hospital down was a shame—we hardly ever lost a patient for any length of time-usually catched 'em before they got to town. Outside the gates, a patient found a tree with a hole in the bottom and hid out in there for about three days before someone caught up with him. The hospital kept most of the dangerous patients in Ward L for the women and Ward #6 for the men.

I 'member I had to work six weeks on the wards to get an idea of ward work and how things ran. I reported to Ward L one night. A nurse told me to help patients undress and get ready for bed. I noticed a female patient having trouble with her buttons and I offered to help.

She said, "I'm watching you."

After the patients went to bed, I sat around with the nurses and one of the staff said, "You know what she meant don't you? She meant if she gets the chance she'd kill you."

"Oh thanks," I said.

I had never heard that before. It was the one and only time I worked on the violent ward for women. I left in 1971, just before Northern State closed. My husband fell off our roof and had a stroke a week later. I took care of him for twelve years until he died. One day I went with my nephew to visit the hospital after it became the Job Corps thing in 1984 or '85, but we didn't get too far. They told us we had to leave. They didn't allow anyone on the grounds unless they had permission.

Postscript: On June 18, 2010, Sally Hinds died peacefully at her home. She was ninety years old.

The hospital labeled the women's wards alphabetically and the men's wards numerically. In 1962, a naming committee proposed adopting the names of favorite Northwest exploreres and pioneers. Wards L & M became Wilkes Hall after lieutenant Charles Wilkes.

Photo: Blanche V. Swalling, 1943

15

At the beauty salon up the road from my house, a conversation ensued between my mother and her hairdresser, Annette. Before long, I found myself pursuing another interviewee; this time Annette's mother, Agnes Harrison.

Bob and Agnes Harrison lived in a one story white farmhouse surrounded by expansive fields. As Agnes invited me into her home, I noticed two floral porcelain teacups and a glass plate of cookies on the dining room table.

"Is it too late in the afternoon for coffee?" she politely asked as she flipped on the coffee maker. Bob poured himself a cup of coffee in his favorite mug and joined us at the far end of the clothed table. Many years ago, a farmer by the name of Robert Harrison lobbied the state to purchase the site for Northern State Hospital. I asked him about this.

"Oh, that would have been my grandfather. He homesteaded this whole area. I remember patients wandered off from Northern State Hospital. They followed the railroad tracks. One nice young man knocked on our door and said, "Could you tell me the way to Seattle?" Not long afterwards, a car from Northern State came and picked him up."

"How could you tell he was from Northern State?"

"Oh," Bob said, pointing to his dungaree overalls, "They wore clothes like this with an insignia on the back."

"Two thousand patients lived there," piped in Agnes. "I felt sorry for them when it closed. People just didn't understand them. Northern State Hospital had been a safe environment for patients."

"You can't describe the flowers," said Bob. "You couldn't paint a picture that pretty. They'd haul manure out of the cow barn in little trailers or wheelbarrows; completely black stuff and they covered the lawn. Come May, the manure turned the grass into the most beautiful green."

Agnes opened her photo album. She had a few postcards of the hospital among her collection, taken by a photographer named Webber. I asked about these.

"Oh, you could buy postcards in the Hub," she explained. I asked about the striking young man in a photo all by himself.

"Oh that was Melrose," Agnes pointed out, "an orderly. He gave tours in the tunnels."

"How old were you in this photo?" I asked.

"I must have been twenty years old. We wore blue and white checked uniforms with a white bib and white apron. I lived there in the fall of 1946. I remember a big snow that winter. We took the patients for walks through the orchards in the fall and let them pick apples. On Saturday, the hospital had dances in the Hub for the patients. One really barbaric thing they did was the electric shock treatments. I don't know how it helped. Years later I worked at Skagit Valley Hospital with Dr. Gruener. Patients were sedated then. They had a ward for epileptics. They considered that a mental illness. Lesbians also had a ward. Students were never allowed on the violent wards. We provided baths and daily hygiene for the patients. We had more freedom at Northern State Hospital than at St. Luke's in Bellingham, as long as we could get in and out of the gate."

"You couldn't be married in nursing school," said Agnes, "but we met boys at the Seven Cedars. Bob and I met on a blind date."

"Did you work at Northern State too?" I asked.

"No, I went into the service," said Bob. "I worked for dad and the logging company. Dad passed away early and I took over the farm. I remember the hospital blew the laundry whistle at twenty minutes after 11 a.m. and twenty minutes after four p.m."

"You could hear the whistle here?"

"Oh!" Bob exclaimed, "You could hear that whistle blow all the way to Lyman. Almost sure, if you needed a job, you could get a job there. I used to drive the school bus and I became acquainted with the doctors. One little first grader fell asleep and I didn't realize he was still on the bus. When I got back to the school, he woke up. I made a special trip to take him back to the hospital where his father worked as a doctor and lived on campus. In those days, the hospital welcomed the people from town. Our kids played baseball up there."

"Our kids sang in the angel choir at church," added Agnes, "and performed up there for the patients. Not long ago, we took some friends to see the place and the security officers stopped us and asked to leave."

"I started the Sedro-Woolley museum," said Bob, "and the hospital donated a lot of things. I got twenty seats from the auditorium."

After this interview, I went to the Sedro-Woolley museum to see their collection of items from the hospital. Bob Harrison's efforts proved to be critical in preserving dozen's of hospital artifacts.

Sedro-Woolley museum 725 Murdock Street, Sedro-Woolley, WA. The museum dedicated one corner to memorabilia from Northern State Hospital: equipment, nurse's outfits, historic photos and doctor supplies.

Photo: M.J. McGoffin, May 18, 2011

The Assembly Hall, built in 1916, hosted social events, movies, church services and performances by the youth of Sedro-Woolley.

Photo: Ron Chamberlain, July 27, 2009

16

The local newspaper carried a story about my research. Before long, I received an email from a reader by the name of Robert Nemo.

"I look at the *Skagit Valley Herald* every day on my computer and ran across your story," he wrote. "It brought back memories."

Since he lived in Oregon, we visited by phone:

I am eighty years old. I worked at Northern State Hospital in 1948 as an attendant while attending Skagit Junior College. I remember everything being regimented. Some attendants abused the patients but once found out, the hospital fired them. On a break one day, I went to 2-South in the Administration building to watch a lobotomy. The surgery room had an observation balcony behind glass. The patient had come from my ward and he did seem to make an improvement.

All kinds of patients lived there; some were alcoholics, some real sad cases. Once I needed to draw a map for a history course in college. A patient overheard me talking and offered to help. He turned out to be a skilled draftsman and helped me score an "A." One patient cut willow branches from Hansen Creek and wove baskets to sell at the commissary store. My daughter still has a baby basket he made. Uncle George Nemo helped the patients build shacks along Hansen Creek where they went to relax. I loved that place. I lived nearby and as an eleven-year old, I wandered across the beautiful, orderly grounds. I visited my uncle Joe Nemo who worked as the head baker and cook. Patients seemed eager for friendship and I never felt afraid playing alone. I knew the violent ward kept an ax killer under lock and key and restrained like a prisoner but most of the patients had free rein to work if they wanted or to enjoy the outdoors. My dad found one asleep in our barn.

One day, I received an e-mail from his daughter, Jane Nemo Latimer regarding the willow doll bed:

My grandmother took me to meet Mr. Jackson, the basket weaver. Mr. Jackson had few or no teeth and always wore a funny looking floppy hat. I have a photo of the Northern State Indians baseball team my Dad played on in 1948-49. The equipment manager was a longtime patient and taught my Dad as a young kid how to play ball. The patient also worked at the chicken ranch. We have him identified in the picture as Dober.

The Northern State Indians baseball team 1948-49:
backrow left to right: Morley Burkett, Crawford,
Joe McCaleb, Ernie Cope, Kenny Jackson, Lee Franks,
Connie Hamilton, Bob Ross, Roy Hassler
Frontrow, left to right: Bob Nemo, Bill Kawaski,
Alloways, George Nemo, Dober.
Building in background is the crematory.

Photo: courtesy of Jane Nemo Latimer

17

I did not have a set plan for the interviews. They just seemed to materialize over time. Every perspective added depth to the story the way layers of paint build up a picture. One of the maintenance crew at the hospital suggested I contact his mother, Janet Coffe Ammons. We met at a coffee shop in Mt. Vernon:

My father worked as the business manager from 1949 to 1950 and we lived in one of the cottages on the hill. I remember two patients, Fred and Ole, who did all the yard work around our place. Fred laid our fires in the fireplace every morning, even in the summer. One day he became very upset because we hadn't burned it and he said we were taking away his job and that nobody liked him! They built a little cabin in the woods nearby and my parents let us visit them and have sandwiches together. Every night, the patients went back to the wards to sleep. We had everything done for us by the patients. No one insane worked in our house, though I do re-member one woman talking to the radio. A woman named Max did all the house cleaning. I think they were happy to be there.

My uncle lived there as a patient but he ran away and no one ever found him. He had spells, you know, and his family had to send him there. My brother-in-law worked there, my uncle and my grandmother.

Northern State Hospital looked just like paradise. I never felt afraid. One of the woman patients yelled at me from behind the sunroom screen to come visit her. Sometimes I did and we talked through the window screen. I visited the Hub with my friends and we went to the shows. The patients ran the canteen store with supervision and they learned skills that way.

The hospital built several wards along the same floor plan. This is Ward #5, built in 1914.
Photo: M.J. McGoffin, November 11, 2009

18

One of my mother's bridge partners, Bonnie Lang, lived at Northern State Hospital as a child. Her father began work as the farm manager in 1950. I traveled to her home in LaConner to visit with her. Children's perspectives are particularly poignant and Bonnie's view of life was like no others:

The workers sometimes called my dad during the night to come help deliver a calf. Every now and then, he asked my sister and me to assist in pulling on the calf's legs. Occasionally, they had to use a block and tackle hooked to a pickup. My dad always warned us to stay away from the sows because they would kill people and tear them to shreds. We brought home a rut piglet once and raised it like a puppy until it was old enough to join the others. We bicycled to the horse barn where we stabled two horses. Patients waded with us through the long grass, bribed our horses in with oats and then saddled them up for us. Whenever we went past the butcher house where they shot animals, we got a creepy feeling.

Once my dad received a different kind of call in the night. One of the foreign doctors had diagnosed a broken leg on a patient at the farm annex. My dad felt over the patient's leg and discovered his pant pockets were just full of tools. The foreign doctors, from Russia or Latvia, didn't understand our slang or our culture. They worked while studying to take the medical boards in this country.

Every morning my mother ordered food for the next day. We never had to go to a grocery store. The farm provided all the food for the patients, employees and their families who lived on the grounds. We lived in the little cottage next to the nurses' dormitory and hiked the goat trail behind our cottage. Trillium, the cross-shaped flower, bloomed on the hill, the first one in the springtime.

We used to watch the nurses, all dressed in their uniforms for the day, leave from Trevennen Hall, across the street from us. Sometimes they babysat us. We walked down a long hedge-lined sidewalk, about ten of us, and waited for the school bus together outside the Administration building steps.

Every night we heard the patients' tortured screams coming from the violent ward across the wide lawn. We wondered what was tormenting them so. The wards smelled like the worst nursing home and some had padded cells. I remember rows and rows of patients in catatonic states just sitting there. Other patients looked like the bag ladies you see today on city streets.

The patients never harmed us and we played quite freely throughout the grounds. Patients worked in our home. It was thought to be therapeutic for them to be around a family—as a step toward normalcy. The hospital staff told us not to talk about their problems because we weren't trained in how to respond.

One day, as my five-year-old sister Claudia walked home, a patient named Pinhead, because of his small shaped head, tried to pull down her pants. She screamed and ran. My dad went to the superintendent and demanded that the patient be locked up, which he was. A few years ago, I saw the patient working in a developmentally disabled workshop here in the valley. I remember a good portion of the patients being under lock and key but many, many patients had freedom of the grounds during the day. Once a patient stole my bicycle and rode to Clear Lake.

A couple years later, we moved to a larger cottage on the hill, above the ponds where people fished. My mother always cooked a great dinner. When she didn't feel like cooking, she sent us to the hospital cafeteria. My mother treated the patients kindly who came to work at our house. I played the piano and a patient came over to listen. She sat down to play and I discovered she had been a concert pianist. She tutored me. Another patient, Ethel, a black woman, used to iron, fold clothes and help with cooking. One day she got mad about something and raised the meat cleaver in a threatening way, violently chopping through the meat on the block. My mother hurried us out of the house and called the attendants who came and took her away.

I remember Helen. She left behind three children and took to us kids because she missed her own so much. It was heart wrenching to watch her. My mother invited her to eat lunch with us but Helen systematically eliminated foods she found unacceptable.

She would say, "Those carrots are poisonous."

We watched her lose weight until finally my mother insisted she eat or go back to the ward. Finally they took her back and gave her a shock treatment. Next time she came, she ate everything. She had forgotten all about her fixation with poisonous food.

We visited the wards at Christmas time to pass out presents and sing carols. The community donated gifts, labeled male or female, for patients who had no family. Some women patients held dolls as therapy. One patient asked me to come to her room to see her doll, which I did. The nurses severely reprimanded me for going into a patient's room.

I worked as a babysitter for the doctors. Dr. Jones lived in the superintendent's mansion, a spooky place to babysit because of all the rooms and dark corners. The mansion sat apart from the campus, surrounded by tall trees and hedges.

Even though Northern State Hospital served the purpose of a mental institution, I want to emphasize that it was not an unhappy place. It was a community. Some patients logged trees on the property, and the woodshops turned the curly maple into beautiful furniture. At the chapel, we sat on a raised platform in the back of the hall, behind the patients and watched first-rate movies. The patients came dressed up in outlandish outfits. At times, the attendants had to subdue them and re-start the movie.

I grew up with the stigma of being "the girl who lived at the bug house." I became a nurse myself and worked with the local geriatric population trying to help them find assisted living placements. When I think back on Northern State Hospital, the place offered sick people a protected environment; the jobs gave them a sense of purpose; the community gave them roots.

Dr. Doughty oversaw the construction of the superintendent's mansion in 1926.
Photo: courtesy of the Department of General Administration, circa 1980s.

19

The hospital gave roots to the children who grew up there as well. I met with Kris Jones Goodan who lived in the Superintendent's mansion in the 1950's. We returned to the vacant field where the mansion once stood. I tried to keep up with her as she ran through the brambles to find the old swimming pool, the secret hiding places in the woods and the horse corral:

I remember an apple orchard near our cottage on the hill. We overlooked a pond and played on a raft in the water. In the winter, we built a bonfire nearby and ice-skated. A few male patients had permission to build huts in the woods. After school, my parents let me talk to a gentle patient named Olin who built a small hut nearby.

In 1950, when my dad was promoted to superintendent, we moved to a fabulous three-story house. One patient worked in the house and disappeared for a few days until we found her, confused in the attic. The second floor had a large guest room for the governor and four big bedrooms. My parents' bedroom opened out onto a sunroom. We spent most of our time there. We played croquet in the garden. My father locked the liquor cabinet but one day he noticed how bottles were pulled out from the bottom. It was never discussed but the hole was fixed.

Patients who worked for us became like members of our family. A delightful German woman named Anna made potholders out of scraps of clothing for every holiday or birthday. She never put filling in them so you needed to use several or you burned your hand. She ironed and made our beds every day. Anna saved all her cookies from lunch for a year and gave them to our neighbors as a gift. Jesse, our cook's helper, played the piano. Every evening, the cooks prepared formal, wonderful meals. One Armenian patient came to clean the bathrooms. Arnold, another patient, had been an alcoholic and completely lost his memory. He vacuumed the house top to bottom every day. It was beyond him to understand instructions. Patients came in the morning, went to the cafeteria for lunch, came back in the afternoon and returned to their wards at four p.m.

Apart from the house, we had an un-fenced swimming pool in a natural pond depression. My mom threw bleach in the water when it rained. I remember a rockery of lilacs and begonias surrounded the pond. We had a big, wonderful swing and tried to catch the dogwood blossoms with our toes as we swung into a nearby tree. We built forts in the woods and crawled under the bushes.

One of the patients left England when her family died of botulism. We discovered she had taught English riding back home and from then on she gave us riding lessons. We rode around the grounds, the former logging trails and all through the woods.

On school days, the children of the doctors, about fifteen of us, met in front of the hospital entrance just outside my father's office. Most of the doctors were displaced persons from Nazi occupied countries. They couldn't get licensed right away to work in this country but they could work at mental institutions. We played games on those grand entry stairs while waiting for the bus. On my way home, I stopped at my dad's office to pick up the mail.

The secretary let me spend a few minutes with my dad. If I had a good report card, the stenographer ladies treated me to a strawberry milkshake at the hub. I sang into the dictaphone and it recorded my voice onto a record. Across the hall, I remember the pathology lab where an employee kept jars of things in formaldehyde. Overall, I lived a charmed childhood. We roller-skated between buildings under the covered walkways. We had the run of the place. So did all the other kids there.

(L) Kris Jones Goodan, daughter of Superintendent Dr. C.H. Jones.
(C) Kris and her brother and sisters.
(R) Kris (five years old) with her brother Herb (three years old) cleaning the swimming pool.
Photos: courtesy of Kris Jones Goodan, circa 1950

20

After the newspaper article about my history project, I waited. Before long, another telephone call. This time from a woman named Marion Solorzano. I now had stories from three girls, unbeknownst to each other: the farmer's daughter, the superintendent's daughter and Marion's point of view as a patient's daughter:

My mother Lillian was born in North Dakota, one of twelve children. She had a third-grade education. Most of her early life she spent working on farms and coming to town on Sundays to give her earnings to her parents. At nineteen years of age, she married Clarence Stenseth in North Dakota and they moved to Day Creek, Washington.

Lillian worked hard clearing a stump farm and planting hay. Clarence drank and terrorized her. I remember mom taking us kids running through the woods to my aunt and uncle's house. We moved into town in 1952 and that's when things started to fall apart. Clarence divorced her and she had no way to support me. The hospital admitted my mother in 1953 due to a nervous breakdown. She was 35 years old.

Clarence got the house and me. I made dad take me to see my mom at the hospital at least once a month. He waited in the car. I ironed shirts for fifteen cents apiece to earn money so I could take mom to the 'soda shop' at Northern State. I loved sitting in the booth with the window. When momma was doing good, we could go and get a hamburger and milkshake together.

I remember the place busy with customers; happy sounds and smiles. One time when I had on a new dress with a taffeta skirt, momma was a little nervous and spilled the whole canister of chocolate shake in my lap. She felt so bad. I didn't care. It was just a dress and I got all wiped off and was fine. I always tried to have enough money so she could buy a pack of cigarettes. I'd write her what I was doing in school, even told her what boy I thought was cute. Momma didn't write me but she told me she liked my letters.

Mom was in a room like a dorm with a long row of beds. I didn't get to go to that part of the building because I was so young, unless a nurse or helper went with me. If she was having a bad spell or really nervous or having shock treatments then I wouldn't be able to see her. Some times we were in a big room with other patients and visitors but with a locked door and an observation area for the staff. As young as I was, they didn't want me to be in the locked room with everyone but I had the paper from mom's divorce that gave me the right to see my mom, so I made sure unless she was really bad I got to see her. They gave my mother shock treatments and had her on Thorazine for seventeen years. She stayed until the hospital closed in 1973. Then they sent her to Delta Rehab where she worked eight hours a day and they took her social security checks.

In 1971 Clarence Stenseth died in a fire in Sedro-Woolley. Once he died, his hold over momma broke and it seemed a devil lifted off her shoulders. She started to really live. Northern State provided a safe place for her. As a kid I hated being teased because my mom was in the "Nut House." I knew my mom wouldn't be there forever. Lillian did the best she knew how and was as strong as anyone. When you are beaten and terrorized for as long as she was, anyone would have broken. I admire her strength, humor and giving heart. In every situation, I ask myself, what am I supposed to learn from this? My mother was not stupid. You could not have known a sweeter person.

The first floor of the Assembly Hall provided a canteen and soda shop.
Photo: M.J. McGoffin, September 22, 2009

21

At a St. Patrick's Day luncheon, I found myself sitting next to Ruth Gross, my sister's mother-in-law. Everyone calls her Grandma Ruth even if they are not related. Ruth worked as a nurse in her husband's clinic. Whenever we had an emergency, we ran to Dr. Richard ("Dick") Gross' office. He was one of the few family doctors who could handle just about anything. Every home football game, you could count on Dr. Gross to bee-line for the bench when a player was hurt. I didn't know how the Gross family found their way to Sedro-Woolley until Ruth shared her story:

In 1956, Richard interned at Seattle's Harborview Hospital and visited Northern State Hospital to help out with hip replacements, surgeries and reading x-rays. We lived at the campus in a duplex for nine months. The hospital provided all our food and patients delivered fresh groceries and flowers once a week. They did light housekeeping in exchange for a little money to spend at the commissary. They might buy toothpaste or get their hair done. When my son Tom wandered off as a toddler, one of the patients brought him home. The patients and staff fished in the ponds, rode buses to town and played on the baseball diamonds. Eventually they decided the patients didn't need to be in a hospital if they were all that well.

22

As a new nurse myself in 1981 at United General Hospital, I met a hardworking L.P.N. named Alberta Swihart. Years later, she contacted me to share her early impressions of Northern State:

In 1936, I moved here from Idaho. I was as green as grass and working under the red roof scared me at first. My first job at Northern State Hospital began in 1960 as an attendant but eventually I earned my license as an LPN and stayed until 1972. When I first started, the hospital kept everything under lock and key. I worked in the treatment ward for women where they used shock treatment. When they began using Thorazine and other medications, fewer people came for treatments. If they took their medications, patients were able to go home on weekends. The old-timers like the geriatric and elderly who couldn't take care of themselves and had nowhere to go, stayed. If a woman was pregnant she went to Memorial Hospital in Sedro-Woolley to deliver her baby and then came back. We never had babies or children there.

23

I began to realize no family in Sedro-Woolley escaped some association with Northern State Hospital. My grandparents immigrated between the wars: two from Poland and two from Lebanon. How my parents met is another story. My Polish grandparents set their hands to a large homestead on Clear Lake Hill and began raising nine children. The girls took their cue from an old-country mother who never questioned her husband. The ones who could, left home. Among the ones to leave was my Aunt Helen. According to my uncle, she married a scoundrel and moved to Seattle where they both worked at Boeing. She tried to raise three young children, but the stress of an ill-advised marriage and hard work began to take its toll. She had a nervous breakdown. He admitted her to Northern State Hospital. Helen was maybe thirty years old. I wondered what she could have done wrong? Why wasn't the husband admitted instead? My family tells me she received shock treatments and they were appalled by the unpleasant living conditions of her ward. Grandpa finally took her to live with him and grandma at the new house in town. Grandpa's shake mill employed mostly men, but Helen started working there too. She split cedar shakes all day, better than most men. The repetitive task seemed to help her heal more than anything else.

24

I met with Arne Erickson, a former hospital nurse, over coffee one day on the recommendation of others I had interviewed. I found Arne to be affable and funny, one of the few people who remembered humorous events at the hospital. Out of his many stories, I gleaned two of my favorites:

After high school graduation in 1964, I went to work in the hospital kitchen where I delivered meals to the wards and supervised a patient crew who washed the dishes. We used electric carts pulled with a tractor, usually driven by one of the patients and plugged the carts in at each ward kitchen. The main hospital was laced with underground tunnels. I discovered I could go between my various dishwashing areas without having to go up and outside. The usual route of travel involved unlocking and locking several sets of doors. By using the tunnels I could move quickly. A patient became upset and complained to my boss in the kitchen because he left me in one area and found me in the next without having seen how I got there since he had traveled the longer upper route.

The Director of Recreation, Shirley House, had this wonderful idea of providing our patients with a change of scenery. She chose unlocked patients from the most regressed units to go camping at Lake Sixteen. We fashioned sleeping bags out of blankets and Shirley received a bunch of donated fly rods. The camp had a dock with swimming barge. The patients lined up on the dock to watch Shirley demonstrate how to cast. Some were exuberant and chatty. One young man in his thirties, named Roger, had been at the hospital for years, and never said a word. His chart described him as uncommunicative. Shirley cast far out into the lake and the patients yelled,

"Do it again! Do it again!"

The next cast dropped all the line at her feet. Every patient keeled over on the dock laughing, including Roger. We put worms on the hooks and the patients simply dropped the lines off the dock. Roger caught the first fish. Within an hour, I had seem him laugh until he almost cried and then run around the dock with his fish, so excited to show everyone.

We gave those patients huge amounts of medications and sleeping medicines on top of that. Why did we do that? It's no wonder they had false impressions of what was going on. Those times were just unreal.

In the mid 1990's, I returned to Northern State Hospital to inspect the laundry facilities at Cascade Job Corps, to the very same room I had washed dishes in with a patient crew thirty years earlier. When my host invited me to see her office, I followed her upstairs to a room I recognized as the place we had performed electro-convulsive therapy years before. I didn't think she needed to know.

A small segment of the original walkway, constructed in 1917, still exists. Most covered walkways have been replaced with metal structures.
Photo: M.J. McGoffin,
July 10, 2009

Deterioration has taken a toll on Wards #4 & #5, built in 1914. So far, they have been spared from demolition.
Photo: M.J. McGoffin, February 4, 2009

25

Anticipating the need for progressive leadership, the State of Washington promoted Dr. Charles H. Jones to superintendent in 1950. He inherited a patient population of 2,139 and a hospital badly in need of reform. For the first time in the hospital's history, the length of patient stays began to decrease. At the same time, however, the hospital embarked on building projects, anticipating institutions would continue to serve the mentally ill. This did not come to pass. Dr. Jones resigned in 1960 and left the practice of psychiatry. He felt mental hospitals still had a role to play and did not believe the community would fully assume the responsibility for patients.

I began to realize not everyone viewed the changes as a good thing.

In the *Mental Hospital Journal*, the editor wrote the following in May of 1960:

> We cannot and must not divorce ourselves from the vast complex of social and community forces that have caught us in their sweep. It appears that the training patterns of the past will not produce the ideal community psychiatrist. While on the one hand striking opportunities are afforded for psychiatrists to lead a fresh and more promising approach to handling the mental disorders, there are also some threats to the integrity and identity of psychiatrist as physicians. To be sure, our modern-day psychiatrist fits the accepted image of a doctor insofar as he superintends a hospital, teaches in a medical school, engages in research, conducts a private practice, and

makes ward-rounds in a white coat. There is evidence that a new persona is crystallizing from the activities of many modern psychiatrists, who appear to be turning into something like physicians to the community. It will be challenging for psychiatric educators in the 1960's to ascertain just what roles psychiatrists are being called upon to play in the community.

One of the younger doctors to embrace the new movement came from Germany and happened to move next door to me. I walked over to visit Dr. Hans Gruener in his castle-style house with bell tower:

In 1942, I read a geography book about Washington State with a picture of Mt. Baker. This piqued my curiosity. I came to Northern State Hospital in 1960 and stayed until it closed in 1972. Most of the wards were open and occasionally an elderly patient wandered away. In my years there, I never saw any patient abuse and only knew of a few dangerous patients. We treated a variety of patients: acute mental breakdowns, chronically ill patients, long-term patients who still had hope of recovery and patients suffering from strokes or brain damage due to illnesses like syphilis. An average day involved meeting patients in new admissions and performing physical exams, then visiting the wards. We took turns being on-call. Northern State Hospital had a behavioral treatment program where patients earned tokens. They never internalized motivation. If they participated in making conversation, they earned a token and exchanged it for the privilege to watch a movie or buy something to eat.

We treated the involuntary admissions from the police departments.

Police from Seattle to Bellingham brought in psychotic people. The local court had to commit them.

In 1960, the new superintendent, trained in the Freudian school of thought, viewed a diagnosis like schizophrenia as a social disease not a brain disorder. I viewed mental diseases as genetically influenced, combined with environmental factors. The variety of symptomatology was fascinating, i.e., the range of what our brain could do. Modern drugs help reduced the agitation and paranoid voice. Society will continue to ask what is the most rational, economic and humane way to treat mentally ill patients. It is a challenge without end.

The government funded a $300,000 project at Northern State Hospital in 1962 to develop a two-year pilot program. Dr. Willard A.E. Larson, the medical director shared the results at the National Institute of Mental Health Conference in 1965 in a report entitled "The Positive Self Fulfilling Prophesy." The following is an excerpt:

An acute mental illness, according to Karl Menninger, need not be a catastrophe, but may be the pivotal experience about which the individual may rally and permanently reorganize his thinking, his personality, and his social relationships with others. We grew to realize orthodox suicidal precautions communicated to the patient that he was untrustworthy. The patient rose to meet the expectation set for him of increasing competence to make his own significant decisions, first within the hospital, and soon without.

Beverly Olson, R.N., participated in the program. During our interview she shared with me her thoughts:

The staff chosen for the project was intuitively empathetic. We attended workshops, readings and discussions. We had no precedent for this program and together we devised a way. Six hundred patients from Snohomish County between the ages of fourteen and sixty years old comprised the test group. The program had two goals: The first goal was to relieve the acute distress of patient in crisis. The second goal was to encourage the patient to regain his ability function. The staff conveyed the expectation that this would be a short hospitalization of one month or less. The patient could expect predictable steps in the program and be able to make observable progress. The staff encouraged patient families to visit.

Several principles undergirded the program: the patient should not endure a depersonalizing experience or loss of identity; the staff expected the patient to function appropriately and exercise self control; the program limited circulation of personal information and respected the patient's right to privacy. The program sought to re-establish normal physiological and psychological functioning. When the patient looked for more stimulation because of boredom, this was a sign of readiness for the next phase: the readjustment period. The patient assumed the responsibility to prepare to return home. He was assigned a counselor who expected the patient to be self reliant and take his own medications. All staff viewed "failure" as a chance to learn. The nurse served as a social catalyst, supporting the patient's emerging leadership qualities and sense of self.

The other state hospitals in Washington tried to emulate the program but failed because it required a non-authoritative approach and their staff resisted it.

After the two-year grant expired, a group of doctors and nurses were contracted to go to Bremerton and the underserved Olympic Peninsula area to set up a community program and implement what we had learned. The Navy hospital took care of the military but not the civilians. Together with the Bremerton community, we decided to provide services for the mentally ill and the retarded at the former Harrison Hospital. We started a rehabilitation unit, a social skills unit and a children's program, especially for autism. We also opened an inpatient children's unit. We provided consultation to Port Townsend and Port Angeles and went weekly to the outlying areas. Now I think it has become a community mental health center with counseling and medication follow-up.

After meeting with Beverly, I felt she and her peers had risen to the challenge of their day with remarkable ingenuity and insight. It is hard to measure the far-reaching benefits the grant had on communities throughout northwest Washington.

26

While attitudes within the mental institution began to change, the general public's did not. *The Everett Herald* of Snohomish County criticized the new "open door" policy at Northern State Hospital where patients were given more freedom to come and go. By contrast, many civic groups throughout Skagit County who had first-hand experience with the patients evidenced no such fear. They took patients to gardens or shopping, hosted luncheons, provided entertainment, bingo parties and birthday events. Dr. William Voorhees, Jr., the hospital superintendent, hosted an open house on May 5, 1967.

"If your picture of the hospital is a wild-haired maniac, a skulking rapist lurking behind a bush about to jump at you, come and see," said Dr. Voorhees. "You won't find one. There aren't any."

27

Despite Dr. Voorhees efforts to reassure a nervous public, he could not stop the shake-down of top management positions, including his own. The newspapers recorded the reverberations coming from the epicenter in Olympia, the state capital, tremors presaging the hospital closure:

January 31, 1968, the *Skagit Valley Herald*: Dr. Saul Spiro, director of the psychiatric residency program at Northern State Hospital stated that Dr. Conte requested his resignation because, for better or for worse, he criticized methods of the department. The present system of centralization was disastrous and under it they were going to leave. A sort of military regimentation was taking place at the hospital in which no one moved until the commander passed an order down through the ranks. "We've been handled in a capricious and arbitrary manner," Dr. Spiro said. Dr. Fred Thompson, chief psychologist said the hospital's efforts to work with community mental health groups had been severely crippled.

January 31, 1968, the *Courier Times*: Senator George Kupka, Tacoma Democrat, heading the legislature's investigation of unrest at the state Department of Institutions promised the employees they would enjoy immunity from reprisals if they chose to criticize policies of the department.

"You need have no fear of speaking out," he said. "We are dealing with issues, not personalities."

Dr. Richard Fredericks, acting superintendent at Northern State Hospital, said that he was concerned with holding the staff together.

"The staff is not sure what is acceptable to the central office," he said. "Rumors the hospital will be closed have been disturbing and disruptive."

Governor Dan Evans appointed Dr. William Conte director of the Department of Institutions in 1966. State Senator Martin Durkan said that the tragic blame for the deterioration must be laid at the doorstep of Governor Evans who had consistently refused to face up to the fact that there was a serious problem in the administration of these institutions.

February 8, 1968, the *Courier Times*: Evans said that the resignations were not unexpected in a time of transition from one administration to another. [Dan Evans, a Republican, defeated Albert Rossellini, a Democrat, in the 1965 Governor's race].

February 15, 1968, the *Courier Times*: The State Department of Institution issued a statement denying the claims of the two men who resigned and attempted to blame them for the conditions which caused their resignation, namely Dr. William Voorhees, superintendent at Northern State Hospital and superintendent Martin of the Rainer School for Retarded Children at Buckley.

February 19, 1968, the *Skagit Valley Herald*: Governor Evans said that he wanted to give his reassurance right from the top that he was going to continue to expand the very fine programs developed in this state. In his opinion, the whole situation was blown up out of proportion.

28

At the same time the State Department of Institutions rattled the superintendents, a young college student worked quietly as an attendant at Northern State Hospital. Little did he know the part his destiny would play. I met Gary Williams to hear his story:

I began work in 1967 and stayed because I fell in love with the patients. I saw patients from the "older" days—patients who had been profoundly impacted by lobotomies and other ineffective treatments. I witnessed the tension between staff who said,

"This is an institution, we tie them down, give them shots and keep them safe," versus staff who believed we should let patients do things for themselves if they were going to return to their communities. In 1971, the Superintendent informed us of the hospital's imminent closing. The political reality was this: Skagit County had two state representatives and Pierce County had nearly twenty. We had no political clout. The state hoped to save millions of dollars by shifting the cost to counties.

The next thing I knew the Sedro-Woolley Chamber of Commerce and the hospital employees sent me to Olympia as a lobbyist for the hospital. The Governor's Office claimed the hospital was an earthquake disaster putting patients at risk, this despite a Department of Institutions report indicating Western State Hospital was a much greater earthquake risk. In the eleventh hour of the budget process one politician offered a deal:

"If you can convince some legislators to vote for my change in the state's purchasing law, I think we can save your state institution."

This was a classic example of political back scratching. I helped him get the votes he needed. We traded the hospital, staff and patients for a bill regarding garbage trucks. As a result, the legislature reinstated the hospital's funding for two years. This gave us time to transition patients in a more thoughtful way. It also bled out some of our best staff because they found better jobs elsewhere.

The state talked of knocking the buildings down. They wanted no chance of any reverse pressure to reopen the institution. When Northern closed, the Legislature allotted special time-limited funding to the five northwest Washington counties to increase their ability to provide services to former hospital patients. It was a small fraction of what the state would have allocated to operate Northern. Those who had forced the closure of Northern billed the transition as forward thinking and commended themselves on a fine job. The community feared having former state hospital patients anywhere near their families.

For the most part, the community mental health centers were neither prepared nor adequately funded. Our clinic in Bellingham received a grant and we hired two marvelous psychiatrists, Nate Kronenberg, M.D., and Gene Rondeau, M.D., from Northern State who recognized their former patients. We also hired two experienced psychiatric nurses and a social worker. Together they served as the core staff. We made the transition from a traditional counseling clinic to that of a comprehensive community mental health center.

We basically reinvented institutional care in the community with several housing options. At two a.m. in the morning, if I had someone in the hospital emergency room, I could call John at the Homestead and he would say "bring her over." He would put her in a bed for the night. We could then sort out the basic daily needs and treatment needs the next day. Most of the time if we had a crisis triage program in place we could avoid a jail or hospital placement.

Operating a residential facility proved to be very difficult because the state only reimbursed approximately $23 a day or less per patient. When folks were in a state hospital, the state didn't get any federal dollars. In community treatment the state leveraged matching funds to obtain federal funds. For a period of time, the community mental health programs just didn't work for the chronically mentally ill. This was not for lack of trying. In Whatcom County, we had only one secure hospital bed for psychiatric patients. We provided sleep therapy for patients in their own homes and helped a lot of people that way.

Western State Hospital was being pressured to resist acute admissions and to send patients back to the community within a few days. I remember one painful time when I drove a patient down to Western and had this conversation with the admitting staff:

"I'm Gary Williams, the liaison for Whatcom County."

"So? What's a liaison?"

"This is one of our patients."

"No he's not. He's a patient of Western State Hospital."

"No. This is a Whatcom County resident and I will be involved in his care."

"No you won't. You are not going to be allowed to be involved in his care."

"This patient is coming home and I'm going to be involved in every step of the process."

We demanded that we participate in the treatment process so when the patient returned home we could assure their success. Another time I remember talking on the phone with a new social worker at Western who said,

"I don't even have to talk with you. You're not even an American. You're from Canada."

I said, "No, I'm in Whatcom County."

She said, "Yes, that's in Canada."

Ahhh—can you imagine what it was like to be a patient?

Today the State and Regional Support Networks have liaisons from every county. When the state enacted a new civil commitment law in 1973, I worked as a deputy commitment officer. The new commitment law provided legal protections. Unfortunately, it created major barriers to providing effective treatment. This profound change in the legal management occurred simultaneously with the closure of Northern. We could only detain them if they were threatening their own life or someone else's or were gravely disabled. If they improved with treatment, they would be immediately released on anti-psychotic medications. Of course, they would be re-detained in short order because they needed weeks of stability not days.

Canada turned back many mentally ill travelers who tried to enter and they ended up in Whatcom County. We weren't keeping our heads above water serving our own folks, so if someone floated in from out of town, like San Diego, we tried to make arrangements with their family and providers in San Diego. I let them know I was putting their family member on the Greyhound and sending them back home. This was known as "bus therapy." A lot of them didn't make it. They disembarked somewhere along the way.

In forty years, we have transitioned from an 800 bed State hospital, with a staff of nearly 600, to over a dozen community mental health centers and residential programs in the area formerly served by Northern State hospital. I believe a measure of the quality of our Northwest Washington communities has been how we adjusted to bringing our folks home. We're not done, but we've made a good start at providing a community safe haven for individuals with major mental illness.

Note: Please see Appendix M for further recommendations by Gary Williams.

29

A friend of mine, Elinor Nakis, told me about a day in 1973 when she boarded a Greyhound bus from the Mt. Vernon station:

"A large group of men from Northern State Hospital boarded at the same time," said Elinor.

I asked her how she could tell they came from the hospital:

They wore outdated street clothes that looked like they had been in storage and were discolored from age. One man sat next to me. He told me the hospital had been closed. His fingernails were long and yellowish-orange and not well groomed but he was clean shaven. The hospital had given him a one-way ticket, along with about forty-five other men. They were in their sixties. He didn't know what he would do when he arrived in Seattle. I got off in Everett so I never knew what happened to him.

30

Northern State hospital closed in 1973 and a second era began: the post-hospital decades. We are good at building institutions; we are not so good at taking them apart. No one knew what to do with a 1086-acre property designed for only one purpose. Ideas sprouted and wilted and transplants had difficulty thriving. The soil had grown only one thing: the idea of an asylum for the mentally ill, an idea now extinct.

For those readers interested in the twists and turns of the following years, I've included those in the appendices. For me, the story ends with the last interview. The setting has been the rainy Skagit Valley; the plot, the rise and fall of an insane asylum; the characters, people like those in our own families.

Swallows migrate each spring to the campus. They build nests in the abandoned buildings, raise their young, and disappear at summer's end. I would not have known this except for a conversation with Landy Morgan, one of the maintenance crew hired in the post-hospital days. I wondered why the birds held such a fascination for him. In time, he told me:

My grandma worked at Northern State Hospital in 1962. My grandpa and I took the Ford Fairlane and headed west, down river, to pick her up each evening. We passed the big yellow gate where a man came out of the guard house. I noticed the ivy growing on the rocks immaculately trimmed on both sides of the road. Men stood around holding rakes and using shovels.

"These men here are not quite right but they are hard workers and these grounds gives 'em self worth, a reason to live," grandpa said.

We drove through Hub Drive and stopped to have a hamburger, fries and malt. Then we watched a movie in the Hub. I mostly watched the patients and moved closer and closer to my grandpa.

In 1977, nine years after my grandpa died, one year after my grandma died, five years after I lost a dear friend in a boating accident, my mom announced she could no longer live with my dad. My family meant everything to me and it was going downhill. Nineteen years old and I needed to talk with God, but I didn't know how. I needed to sit in a happy place, a place that held

The gatehouse building continued the Spanish Colonial Revival architectural style.
Photo: Blanche V. Swalling, 1943.

103

fond memories. I chose the entrance to Northern State. No one was out trimming the ivy, no one holding rakes. But there were the familiar white specks against that warm blue sky. The cattle field smelled the same and the pond looked the same. I looked at familiar sights through blurry eyes. Northern State Hospital had closed four years earlier. The ivy along the road showed neglect and the barbed wire fence and its cedar posts struggled to stay up. I sat there in my 1969 Ford pickup and cried and talked to God. The swallows darted in and out of the tall grass. I watched those birds for the longest time. At 8:30 p.m. time stopped. As I was looking up at all these white-breasted swallows against that sky, I was told everything would be fine. If I was given some guidance, I promised not to disappoint.

I pulled out and drove down the hill. It was a different trip down than it was going up. I felt better. I did not question how or why. For the next nine years, I mended some wrongs. I found and married the girl I'd been looking for. I applied for a job with the state in June of 1987, where else but Northern State Hospital. Whenever I could get away from my regular workload, I worked on the front entrance, trimming the ivy on both sides of the road. I saw to it that the field was cut and mowed.

When I first came to work, I noticed records kept on the carpenter shop door. I found it fascinating the dates consistently documented the return of the swallows between March 10th to the 25th and the dates for departure in September. We kept the tradition going. The return of the swallows for me is more than a date on the carpenter shop door. It is spiritual.

Yesterday, March 16th, the date went on the door. The first returnees we call the "scouts" or "sentries." They fly up and check out weather conditions and then "report" back, back where, I don't know yet, maybe Roseburg,

The carpenter's shop, built in 1933, is in the center of the facilities cluster.

Photo: Ron Chamberlain, September 10, 2009.

The powerhouse initially burned wood scrapes from the property and later bought coal from local sources. Today, the powerhouse buys electricity and natural gas.

Photo: M.J. McGoffin, November 19, 2008

Oregon. The Scouts show up and then disappear for a couple days. Today, none; yesterday, four. The white breasted ones show up every March and, when they do, the date goes on the door, and only the swallows see the tears of happiness I shed.

Landy arranged for me to visit one afternoon to see the swallows for myself. It is not a common thing to sit at a well-worn table with seven men in matching green shirts, in the lunchroom of a 1915 steam powerhouse. In the one-hundred-year history of this room, I doubt many women had. I wondered if the table had ever been entirely cleared and wiped down. Items seemed to have piled up like an overstocked thrift store. Today I noticed a dictionary, half-empty bottles of condiments and assorted used coffee cups. The men seem to have assigned seats by habit. One chair had been left vacant for me.

Apparently, two swallow scouts had been spied and the rest of the flock should arrive within days. As it turned out, I didn't see a single swallow. I did, however, see a pack of men, bound by common bonds as only men could do. I was in the presence of engineers, plumbers and electricians according to their state job descriptions. According to each other, they were handymen of the first order. They patched, salvaged and improvised ways to keep the buildings together. One employee ate his lunch while still wearing the safety harness that clasped him to ropes on the roof. He didn't seem to notice the carabiners dangling off his body like Christmas ornaments. I looked at the crew who kept the lights on and heat working to the tenants, propped up the historic remaining buildings against further deterioration and maintained nearly two hundred acres of landscape. One thing they did not need was me disturbing their brotherhood.

My guide tried to break up the unease in the den. He threw sliced apples to the men like an alpha wolf to his pack. Later he explained that job lay-offs had been frequent. The man with the least seniority in the room wore his apprehension like a fugitive. Still, they tolerated me until lunch was over then folded up their lunch boxes, scattered out the doors and disappeared into the buildings.

In 2004, Sedro-Woolley High School history teacher, Karl Heuterman inspired three seniors, Michael Hennings, Brittany Bazinet and Ashley Baumgardner, to raise the money to purchase the hospital cemetery plaque.
Photo: Ron Chamberlain, August 8, 2009

EPILOGUE

If we concede that every image, every voice, every sound, every touch registers in our brain and the brain sorts out all the sensory input in endless ways, combining data with a stew of neurochemicals and storing everything in a unique filing system, a dis-eased mind, at one time or another is not unlikely. We tell each other to get a grip, pull yourself together, buck up, get mentally tough, when in fact we may feel like we are falling apart, on the edge, losing our mind, disintegrating or overwhelmed. When circumstances conspire to tip us over the edge, most of us recover our equilibrium, but it is a balancing act throughout our lifetimes. Just like an electrical outlet will short-circuit, life can trip our breaker box. Anyone of us can fall into the cloudy waters of mental illness during a crisis. Some are able to crawl out onto the banks on their own; others seem to be caught in a riptide always pulling them away from the shore's safety. We avoid people with mental illnesses—afraid we will get pulled down into their chaos.

Mental diseases frustrate the best medical scientists because they present the greatest unknown frontier; we are largely our genetic composition but the interaction with environment plays out in unpredictable ways. Northern State Hospital left us a legacy of ideas; one of them being the healing effect of a life lived closely with the seasons and purposeful work.

Today, the Steelhead Club hosts a children's fishing derby each spring at the hospital ponds, an opportunity for children to feel the tug of a wild, silvery fish on their lines, not unlike Roger's exhilarating experience so many years before. Amy Lanning, the Life Skills instructor at Sedro-Woolley High School, mentioned to me that her older students needed a place beyond her classroom, an environment simulating the real world. I knew one of the staff cottages at Northern State was vacant and Amy and her colleagues moved in to practice life skills. The students, despite their various disabilities, delighted at the sight of a herd of deer in the backyard of their cottage.

In the early years, hospital patients raised chickens, collected the eggs and painted them for the town's Easter celebration. On Easter morning, the patients watched from a bus as the town's children fanned out across the high school football field, running for the decorated eggs. The patients on the bus might have been Fred and Ole, Helen, Lillian, Mr. Jackson or Roger, men and women, fellow beings struggling to live a full human life against great odds.

Howling coyotes still unnerve me; hospital cemeteries not so much. I may know a few patients there: Anna, the potholder lady, Eric from the seacoast or Dober, the baseball player. I imagine they are spirit guardians of the landscape.

Appendix A: The *Courier Times*, 1958

I included the following newspaper account because the report portrays a mental institution at its peak just before its descent. Patients and staff alike had no inkling of the radical changes to come in the next decade. The *Courier Times* dedicated an entire issue to Northern State Hospital (NSH). Several department managers submitted short summaries, included here in abbreviated form:

NSH received the Mental Hospital Achievement award for having made the most advances despite adverse conditions. Only four hospitals, three in the United States and one in Canada, received this recognition from the American Psychiatric Association. The hospital claimed a cure rate of 67%. Among the treatments available at the institution, doctors used electroshock therapy, insulin coma therapy, psychotherapy and psycho-pharmacological therapy. Over the last four years, the patient population decreased from 2237 to 1729, creating a ratio of 2.89 patients per employee. The x-ray department acquired new equipment and within the last few years the number of x-ray exposures increased 333%. The hospital expected to complete a new clinical laboratory designed for an increased staff to conduct research on mental disease. Psychologists no longer only administered psychological tests but also conducted group psychotherapy, provided nurse lectures, performed electroencephalographs, lead research projects and staff conferences. In order to retain qualified staff, the hospital reclassified professional salaries to become more competitive with other states.

The accounting office received the money and personal effects of all patients and stored them in a vault. When a patient left the hospital, he received his money back after the state deducted money for any dental work, glasses or clothing the patient purchased.

The commissary manager, Otto W Mandahl reported,
"I have witnessed a decided change in the clothing, feeding and treatment of ward residents."

The hospital provided a greater variety of food within a domestic atmosphere. Treatment seemed to be more scientifically based. Patient clothing no longer consisted of drab uniforms but displayed a variety of options.

The laundry manager credited his department with contributing to a patient's positive outlook by providing clean, neatly pressed clothing. Over the past ten years, metal washers with safety devices replaced the old wooden ones. The hospital anticipated needing a more complete modernization of the laundry building. To further well being and personal pride, NSH offered a beauty salon and barbering service for the patients.

On the first Tuesday of each month, the food service department sent a cake to each ward to honor patient birthdays. Patients expressed appreciation for this special consideration. Employees supervised forty men and twenty women in the main kitchen. The food service department reported that each meal cost twenty-seven cents. On Thanksgiving, the kitchen prepared 3200 pounds of turkey.

According to Jim Evans, supervisor for the grounds and greenhouse, to maintain the forty acres of lawn required a crew of seven employees and more than sixty patients, both men and women. Evans described the patients as usefully occupied while getting exercise and fresh air instead of being left in the wards. In the spring, the crew applied over three hundred tons of barnyard fertilizer, in addition to commercial fertilizer. They set out 45,000 bedding plants and 10,000 bulbs. In the fall and early winter his department organized a leaf-raking program. Some of the leaves the crew mulched by a rotary mower and returned to the ground, the rest yielded 50-100 tons of fine textured compost for the greenhouse and flowerbeds. Each month, the crew sent 30-500 plants to the wards and institution rooms. At Christmas time, they provided 500 wreaths and over 2000 feet of cedar rope to decorate the hospital along with a 100 poinsettias grown in the greenhouse.

"We have three main reasons to be proud of our industrial assignment program," stated Glen Coggins, the supervisor of the industrial assignment program. "The unquestionable therapeutic values involved; the economic operation of the hospital, and the fact that other institutions have visited NSH to examine our assignment system expressing much interest in the way the program operates."

Prior to 1950, according to Mr. Coggins, little value seemed to be placed on the assignment of patients. The system grossly over staffed some areas with part time helpers, resulting in idleness and confusion. Other work areas remained understaffed causing resentment and work poorly done. He credited Dr. C.H. Jones with improving the system. In 1950, the patient population had reached 2,200 with only 650 patients engaged in work. By 1958, the census dropped to 1,750 but the hospital assigned nearly 850 patients to fifty different work areas.

Gerald Simpson department head of maintenance reported that the hospital had nearly 4000 feet of tunnel system carrying steam lines, hot water lines and some of the electrical system from the powerhouse to most of the buildings on campus. In 1957 they completed the construction of the new boiler plant and had plans to replace 7000 ft of wooden pipe. The city of Sedro-Woolley completed a new sewer trunk line to the hospital in 1957. In the past year they dredged Hanson creek from the concrete highway bridge to the cannery, moving 20,000 yards of gravel. Mr. Simpson's crew consisted of 26 employees and 26-35 patient helpers. The work therapy for the patients he considered a very important part of their treatment program.

"We see the concrete evidence of this almost daily," he said.

The maintenance department removed some of the old hazardous covered walkways at the hospital and installed new ones. Workers replaced terrazzo floors with wooden ones. Mr. Coggin's department kept track of the 2500 locks and keys used at the institution. The sawmill under his department often traded lumber for other products such as plywood.

Louis Bernard, the farm manager boasted, "The Northern State Hospital blue ribbon cattle herds, the poultry house, the piggery, the dairying activities and the cannery are all operated both as a therapeutic value to patients and an economic necessity."

The hospital employed 694 people and spent $500,000 in the community for supplies and services. Local companies provided most of the labor to remodel the hospital buildings. Governor Albert D. Rossellini urged every voter in the state to approved referendum No.10 on November 4, 1958 to raise money for construction projects at state institutions. NSH requested $2.5 million to build Douglas Hall.

"We can take pride in the fact," says Sedro-Woolley mayor Eugene Kriskov, "that the efficient work and treatment by the staff and employees of this institution have made it one of the finest state mental institutions in the nation. When we realize that this hospital brings somewhere near 2.2 million dollars a year in payroll to the Sedro-Woolley area, it is easy to contemplate what would happen to our local economy without it. I urge all people of Sedro-Woolley and the surrounding area to dwell on this point for a moment and realize what this institution means to each one of us."

Appendix B: Hospital newsletter

Reading through the *Northern State Hospital Newsletter* of July 1964, a publication printed in the Occupational Therapy department, sounded more like a social calendar at a senior community center than a mental institution. Each ward had a patient reporter who submitted news in a decidedly upbeat tone:

News from Barkley Hall: The grand and glorious 4th of July weekend is here, with never a dull moment and entertainment every minute. Three times we went to Sedro-Woolley! Thursday night, the *Hootenanny Hillbilly Mountaineer Band* and the choosing of the Loggerodeo Queen; Friday the rodeo bronco-busting and Sunday afternoon the Loggerodeo. What a marvelous time we had.

Colman Hall: We welcomed five new women from Douglas SW: Three women left our ward and moved to Barkley Hall. We all miss these ladies and hope they find their new homes pleasant and enjoyable.

Elliott 1 Hall: Weather and our moods can be a real interesting subject for thought.

Elliott 2 Hall: We had a hugely successful concession over at the recreation building during the carnival. The student nurses did a bang-up job of decorating the ward and the booth at the party. Our group went down to pick strawberries one afternoon on the south forty and then had strawberries and cream.

Thompson 2 Hall: Mrs. Cahill of volunteer services took eighteen of our ladies to the parade downtown.

Wilkes Hall: Those who went on the fishing-camping party from Wilkes hope to go again. The occupational therapy department hosted a party July 3rd on the occasion of Mrs. L. Dahl's retirement. Guests played bingo and winners received prizes of candy bars or cigarettes of their choice.

The hospital set up tables on the lawn with attractive bouquets in red, white and blue. The kitchen provided a picnic menu: baked beans, potato salad, relish plate, wieners, buns and cheese. The floats, marching bands and decorated cars assembled for a well-paced, happy, friendly parade through campus.

The men on Valdes Hall 2 are building a mock-up of the old Skagit River railroad. The model will include mountains, rivers, streams, dams, logging operations, towns, farms and landscaping. Anyone with used train parts or material may take them to Valdes Hall.

We have a variety of dances going on here in the recreation building. Please consult your recreation schedule and come join us.

Appendix C:
History of the Cascade Job Corps Program

The hospital closure contributed hundreds of lost jobs to an unemployment in Skagit County reaching 14.8 percent by 1975. In response, Governor Dixie Lee Ray appointed Bill Shuler to hire a coordinator for a program called the Economic Development Association. Bill hired Ian Munce, an attorney and newcomer to the county and re-opening Northern State became his first project.

In 1973, the federal government invested in job training as a way to pull out of the recession. Congress passed the Comprehensive Employment and Training Act (CETA) with the Young Adult Conservation Corps (YACC) as a sub-category. The YACC provided job experience for youth while performing needed conservation work on public lands. The participants lived in-group residences and developed interpersonal and life skills.

"Ian started pulling strings at Senator Magnuson and Jackson's offices. We submitted a study to show how monies from different sources could be mixed together," stated Bill. Mr. Munce obtained $100,000 in impact funds to study a way to replace nearly 600 jobs lost by Northern State Hospital's closure. He consulted a Seattle architectural and engineering firm, Mann, Millegan, Morse and Ramsey on the feasibility of renovating the historic wards to house the Young Adult Conservation Corps program. The consultants determined that they could be renovated at one-third to one-half the cost of new construction. Mr. Munce helped raise nearly $4.5 million dollars in federal and state funds to remodel approximately 200,000 square feet of buildings.

In 1977, Camp Cascade, the YACC program, officially opened, welcoming 400 participants and an annual budget of $6 million dollars. Proponents of the YACC program noted enrollees returned $1.09 worth of work for every $1 of taxpayer money spent. YACC's Camp Cascade became the largest one of its kind in the country and the only one jointly administered by two federal agencies: the Department of Agriculture's Forest Service and the Department of the Interior's National Park Service. In addition, the YACC, as a job-training program also fell under the auspices of the Department of Labor.

Yet a fourth player entered this complicated relationship of agencies: Skagit Valley College. Bill Shuler moved on to became the director of Skagit Valley College's programs at Northern State Hospital. He helped secure federal Comprehensive Employment and Training Act (CETA) funds to provide enrichment services for the Young Adult Conservation Corps participants.

"The Northwest Regional Council funded several hundred thousand dollars for human service programs and we secured monies for job training," said Bill.

The college served as the local sponsor of these federal funds to pay for:

- Recruiting minorities and selecting the enrollees for the YACC
- Providing career guidance, job placement and dormitory assistance
- Security and camp safety
- Crew supervision
- Administrative support
- Industrial First Aid

- Basic carpentry
- Chain saw operation
- Van and bus driving
- G.E.D. program instruction and personnel supervision courses.

The college had its sights set on occupying Trevennen Hall, the former nurses' quarters. The building would serve as their east county presence and give them space to expand their operations. The college anticipated continued funding from state and federal sources and the ability to develop occupational programs for the YACC students. "They were kids with problems, most smoked marijuana or worse," stated Barbara Ward-Thompson. "Most were urban kids from dysfunctional families who didn't know diddily about working. The kids needed counselors on the ward to talk to at night so that is how we staffed it."

One such course of study, called the Human Services Program, developed by Bill Shuler, provided training in mental health treatment and alcoholic rehabilitation. Clinical rotations occurred at the PORTAL and Pioneer programs.

"Through the Federal Comprehensive Training Act, I secured additional funding in 1979 for PORTAL," said Bill. A second program served the involuntary chronic alcoholic client through a contract with the Pioneer Cooperative Affiliation.

As proponents knitted innovative programs into the fabric of the former hospital, a new name seemed in order and "The Northern State Multi-Service Center" replaced "Northern State Hospital."

With great fanfare, Ian Munce, who served as the secretary of the steering committee, invited the community to a grand opening of the Northern State Multi-

Purpose Center on September 1, 1979. They expected all elected officials who had been a part of the process to attend: Senators Henry Jackson, Warren Magnuson, Governor Dixie Lee Ray, Congressman Al Swift, State Senator Lowell Peterson, state representatives Jerry Vrooman, Duane Berentson and Mary Kay Becker. Event organizers celebrated the day with entertainment and games including a footrace, a blue grass band, balloon toss, grand prize drawings, the Vela Luka Croatian Dance Company, Knudson's Big Band and a tug of war over the pond between the elected officials and public citizens. The hosts served a picnic lunch of BBQ chicken, baked beans, potato salad and Pepsi-Cola. Despite the success of the day, Bill and Ian reserved a measure of caution.

"We knew the Young Adult Conservation Corps program would be a temporary thing. We concluded a similar-type program would work and Senator Henry Jackson suggested a Job Corps center to succeed the Young Adult Conservation Corps program. This is when Ian really began to shine," said Bill.

The Young Adult Conservation Corps transitioned into the Cascades Job Corps program in 1981. A private company contracted with the U.S. Department of Labor to provide vocational, academic and social skills training to young men and women between the ages of 16 and 22.

Within the short time span of a few years, Ian Munce achieved the extraordinary accomplishment of resuscitating life at the former hospital with an infusion of new programs and funds. Today, the Cascade Job Corps Program anchors the campus as the major tenant.

"If you had to identify one person who brought the Job Corps program to Northern State Hospital, it would have to be Ian," said Bill.

Cascade Job Corps renovated the former Men's Occupational Therapy department into a new use for their students. Several historic buildings now serve a population of nearly 300 students.

Photos: (top) Photo of Men's Occupational Therapy Building courtesy of General Administration circa 1950s.
(bottom) Bob's Pool Hall photo by M.J. McGoffin. August 5, 2009.

Appendix D: PORTAL

A program close to the hospital's mental health origins emerged under the care of Dr. Fred Thompson who served as the chief psychologist at Northern State Hospital from 1954-1973. During those years, his intermediate program helped prepare patients to be discharged by emphasizing personal responsibility. This concept evolved into the Program Offering Rehabilitation Training and Adult Living (PORTAL) in 1979.

"Fred had this special empathy for long-term schizophrenia patients," stated Barbara Ward-Thompson:

> They needed a safe place to live where they were comfortable but they needed to learn life skills too. He housed his patients in a building by the farm. "You can stay here as long as you want," he would say, "but when you feel ready to leave you can leave." Some stayed while some moved out into the community. Sometimes the patients wore out their families until they couldn't take care of them anymore.

With Dr. Thompson's sudden and untimely death in 1981, Donna Gilkey acted as temporary superintendent until Dave Evans assumed the permanent position. Most of the policy rules and restrictions began as client suggestions. The program philosophy encouraged clients to exercise their right to give feedback to the staff.

By 1989, PORTAL had developed sheltered workshops in janitorial services, woodshop, upholstery, food services, newspaper services, clerical, furniture stripping and refinishing, screen-printing for garments, posters and signs, a sewing shop serving the health care, restaurant and motel industries with quantity orders of aprons, adult care bibs, laundry bags and tote bags. Patients earned money in the workshops. Further training included daily living skills and personal hygiene. The "Step System" run by Randy Hansen of Western Washington University offered classes in cooking, anger management and problem solving. Clients could also earn credits at Skagit Valley College with tuition paid in part by PORTAL. The program provided recreation facilities and off-site field trips.

PORTAL occupied the six buildings in the center of the campus. In 1990, PORTAL operated the kitchen and dining facility, providing meals under contract to Cascade Job Corps and Pioneer North, the other residential programs on campus. The dining facility served an average of 2,000 meals per day.

"The PORTAL program tried to integrate the patients more into the community," Barbara explained. "Fred insisted patients come into town and buy their clothes, go to a ball game, get ice cream. Every now and then a patient walked away without paying and got him or herself in trouble. Fred would get a call and quickly drive over to fix the problem. He worked hard to develop relationships so he would have places for the patients to work at. The patients didn't threaten people."

PORTAL provided a 146-beds for voluntary rehabilitation and treatment. About ninety percent of the residents were diagnosed with schizophrenia. At its peak, PORTAL treated 200 people per year with severe mental problems. Clients stayed from six to eighteen months, sometimes longer in certain cases. They made payments to the state for mental health services in accordance with their ability to pay. Most clients were assessed no charge. The daily cost of treating clients for addiction and mental illness averaged $85.00 per day. The program generated 170 local jobs and a $3.5 million payroll.

"After ten years," according to Barbara, "PORTAL was discontinued too. The state thought these services could be transferred over into the community."

State budget cuts factored in the closure as well. PORTAL closed on December 31, 1993.

Ground preparation for the construction of the Douglas building.
Photo: courtesy Department of General Administration, 1961

PORTAL occupied the modern Douglas building added in 1962 to the main entrance of the hospital.
Photo: M.J. McGoffin, December 1, 2008

Appendix E: Ten proposals

On December 14, 1984, the Skagit Council of Governments (SCOG) sponsored a conference to hear ten proposals for the Northern State Multipurpose Center:

- A private psychiatric hospital. Current projections estimated a substantial need for additional short-stay psychiatric beds in residential settings.

- Rehabilitation facility for children and youth. The facility would be short-term residency for counseling and life style learning of ambulatory clients.

- University of Washington comparative medical resource facility: The Division of Animal Medicine program needed off-campus animal housing and rearing facilities to support biomedical teaching and research. A joint venture with Skagit Valley College could train veterinary assistants.

- Natural Resources Youth Camp. Several agencies including the Soil Conservation Service and the Department of Agriculture supported the summer program. They needed facilities for one week to house and feed 100 junior high and high school age youths, plus 20-30 staff. The program provided recreation and exploration of the local ecology.

- Recreational Vehicle Park: Great American Adventure, an R.V. park chain, expressed interest in Northern State Campus as a regional site. They required acreage above the flood plain.

- Skagit County Fairgrounds. A site selection committee appointed by the Skagit County Commissioners to relocate the Skagit County Fair determined the former dairy farm buildings and surrounding land met the requirements. Consultants included members of the Lynden Fair Board, Sedro-Woolley Public Works employees and Skagit County Fair Board members.

- Veteran's Administration Facilities.

- Entrepreneurial Business Incubator : Bill Shuler, Executive Director, Skagit County Community Action Agency, Hal Pullin, Special Program Coordinator, S.C.C.A.A., Burt Williamson, Director of Vocational Education, Skagit Valley College and Peter Stroosma, Director of the Business Resource Center, presented their case.

- Conference and Technical Center. Skagit County needed an area to provide overnight accommodations, food service, and classroom space. The campus could also be used for Elderhostel educational and cultural programs for senior citizens.

- A Pacific Rim Peace Center. The site could provide for conferences and academic internships focusing on peace studies, education and conflict resolution.

Dr. Jones, and Dr. Aldrich, the conference organizers, requested in a letter to Ian Munce, the secretary of Skagit County of Governments, $36,000 to conduct a feasibility study of these proposals to be presented in April of 1985.

Appendix F: The Norlum Foundation

I came across the minutes from sixteen years of monthly meetings, thanks to Barbara Ward-Thompson's help. The Norlum Foundation incorporated on April 11, 1984. The foundation levied dues of $25/year. It secured a three-year lease from the state to use the superintendent's mansion.

The immediate task of readying the former Superintendent's mansion involved restoring heat, adding an emergency exit on the second floor and renovating the third floor to house a custodian to guard against vandalism. The water line needed to be re-connected and the basement had ground water seeping into the billiard room.

In 1987, the group agreed to spend $250 to recruit military school officials to look at the campus as a possible military institute.

In 1988, the foundation hosted the Economic Development Association of Skagit County's (EDASC) quarterly dinner meeting for 387 banquet guests at the former hospital. Dr. Jones invited the audience to become Norlum Foundation members and further the cause of their mission. He anticipated a world-class rhododendron arboretum on the Northern state campus.

In 1990, the members learned of asbestos in the mansion. In November, pipes froze and the water lines broke. In light of new evidence of crumbling cement on the north wall and staircase dry rot, the group decided to abandon the mansion. An engineering survey in 1989 suggested the mansion alone required over one million dollars in renovation costs. The members decide to direct their efforts to other projects. The foundation also pursued discussions with Pam Carnahan, Superintendent of Sedro-Woolley schools, to locate a new high school on the property.

Nick Cockrell from General Administration (GA) suggested the Norlum Foundation help with the cemetery. G.A. was to receive $4000 from the Charitable, Educational, Penal and Institutional Trust Fund to take care of the cemetery. In 1993, the group intended to landscape the cemetery.

On September 8, 1993, Dr. Charles Jones died at his home in a fall from a tree. The foundation received $960 towards a memorial in his name. They installed a memorial granite pillar with brass plaque in an area of the hospital re-named the "Dr. C.H. Jones Memorial Park."

In 1993, the foundation had 129 due paying members from towns across Skagit Valley and beyond: doctors, nurses, dentists, former employees of the hospital, business owners, college presidents, mental health counselors, school superintendents and teachers, government officials, accountants, lawyers and journalists. The treasurer's report totaled $6626.00.

In 1994, ideas for Skagit County's recently acquired land included: a skeet shooting range, midget car track, interpretive center, archery range, indoor shooting range, concert area, expanded golf course and fair. Unfortunately, forty-six percent of the land turned out to be wetlands. The county proposed developing two hundred of the acres. One idea suggested reserving fifty-three acres for the high school.

In 1995, the high school idea was off the table. By 1998, members discuss disbanding. Suggestions on how to disburse funds included donating to the Sedro-Woolley Museum's hospital exhibit; creating a scholarship for Job Corps students interested in pursuing a career in human services or mental health and contributing to the county's recreational plans or the Cook Road playfields.

Appendix G: Neurological Center Pilot Project

In 1986, in an effort to address the long term needs of neurologically impaired persons, the Senate allocated $30,000 to the Skagit Council of Governments (SCOG) for the Northern State Neurological Center Pilot Project. Jerry Vrooman, the project manager submitted a final report in June of 1987. The mission of SCOG was to generate economic growth. They looked for ways to revitalize the under-used property at Northern State Hospital.

The report suggested the neurologically impaired person's needs were not being met at psychiatric hospitals, nursing homes or in the community. Neurologically impaired adults included all people over eighteen years of age who experienced brain impairment and depended on others for care and decision making. This included people with degenerative diseases of the brain, the central nervous system, permanent brain damage from cerebrovascular accidents, trauma, infection, anoxia, tumors or substance toxicity.

The report identified the many support groups available to families in the region of Skagit, Snohomish, Island, San Juan and Whatcom counties. However, the report found that adults with neurological impairments were given lower priority than those with severe mental illness in the community mental health system. They recommended remodeling Barkley Hall at a cost of $954,387.00 to serve as a long-term residential facility. Family members interviewed stated they often waited too long before seeking help and became exhausted both emotionally and financially. They sought help to better understand and deal with their family member but they did not desire government intervention in their lives. The families did not request long term residential facilities. Yet the study concluded a state funded facility should be made available for this population. No action came of this pilot project and Barkley Hall has since been demolished.

Appendix H: County Fair

Excerpt from a *Skagit Valley Herald* article by Seth Preston, staff writer, August 7, 1986:

If the Skagit County Fair is moved, its new home will be at Northern State Hospital near Sedro-Woolley, the County Commissioners agreed Wednesday. But such a move depended on creating a new management structure and finding money within the next few years. The commission's unanimous vote was followed by loud applause from a large group of Sedro-Woolley residents who had pushed the former state mental hospital campus as the best location for a revamped fair. Commission Chairman Rohrer a Sedro-Woolley resident, made the motion to select a proposed 110-acre parcel at the hospital.

A report prepared by Budget Director Mike Woodmansee said the county doesn't have enough money on hand to spend for duplicating the current fair site elsewhere, let alone expanding it at another location. The cost to duplicate present fairgrounds facilities at Northern State was listed at $655,000 in the environmental impact statement. In addition, the county would have to subsidize losses of up to $300,000 during the first few years of operating a revamped fair, he said. Woodmansee said grants were available, and bonds could be issued if voters approved. Voters also could favor special property tax levies or raise the ceiling on property taxes. Woodmansee's report recommended not using any money from a $1.1 million fund set aside for land acquisition and facility improvement.

The county needed the money for future projects such as renovating the Courthouse Annex.

"If we have to cross all the bridges before we come to them, we sure as hell are never going to make the trip," said Sedro-Woolley businessman Al Doorn.

"Move the fair and let it grow," suggested Sedro-Woolley mayor Don Walley. "It can't grow where it is."

The horse barn, built in 1929, had stanchions for sixteen horses and storage room for tackle.
Photo: M.J. McGoffin, April 22, 2007

Appendix I: A Blueprint

In 1988, General Administration (G.A.) requested and received funds to conduct a study on the possible uses of the campus and to develop a "blueprint" for operation of the property:

- G.A. should continue to operate the facility as a multi-use campus. It should consider a change in ownership only if another agency can and will operate the entire campus. Due to the large size of the campus, it is unlikely that one program or agency could afford to operate the entire space and multiple ownerships would cause both logistical and operating difficulties. The infrastructure systems, although antiquated, were generally in good repair and could be upgraded without major investment.
- The 230-acre campus represented considerable value to the state in both land and improvements. Nearly sixty percent of the buildings were occupied with almost five hundred residents and two-hundred fifty staff daily using the campus.
- 25-30 acres were available for construction of other buildings to support state and local government, or a combination of public and private activities.
- The cost to dismantle the campus buildings and infrastructure was estimated at more than $10 million, an amount greater than improvements needed to continue operation of the campus; demolition of the entire campus would

remove almost 400,000 square feet of space currently used for social service and educational programs.

- Ten of the forty buildings on the campus were vacant and generally not suitable for renovation due to structural deficiencies.

- Base costs for occupancy during 1992 were estimated at $3.00 per square foot.

- The campus was zoned for "general use." The local community should continue to be involved in discussions related to use of Northern State lands.

Appendix J: The Regional Support Network

In 1988, local lawmakers planned to pursue funds to renovate two buildings at the former Northern State Hospital into a facility to house 100 long term patients. Jules Sugarman, the Department of Social and Health Services director, objected to the site of NSH and disagreed with the projected costs of renovating the old buildings.

On October 6, 1989 Patricia Snyder testified to the Washington State Health Care and Correction committee. She requested two 15-bed evaluation and treatment facilities for acute mentally ill, one each in Snohomish and Whatcom Counties. She appealed for 120 long-term care rooms at the former Northern State Hospital to be operated by a mental health provider under contract through a consortium with the Region III counties. To reach the minimum state standard for community mental health would cost $10.6 million of state funds in the first biennium, $27.7 million of state funds in the second, and $33.9 million in the third. Capital cost to develop two evaluation and treatment buildings and renovate facilities at Sedro-Woolley was estimated to be an additional $5.5 million in the first biennium.

On October 26, 1989, five member counties formally signed an inter-local agreement forming the North Sound Regional Support Network (NSRSN) led by Ruth Wylie who chaired the Board of Directors. Senate Bill 5400 required the Board of Directors to begin serving 85% of the residents within Region III by July 1993. Region III included Island, San Juan, Skagit, Snohomish and Whatcom Counties.

To access the $2.5 million legislated for development of the 120 long-term care beds at the Northern State Multi-Service Center campus, General Administration had to lease with a Regional Support Network. "We have a mandate from legislators to use Northern State," said County Commissioner Ruth Wylie. "The Legislature wants patients treated at the county level with Western and Eastern State hospitals used only for the most complicated, long-term cases."

Only a small portion of the northeast corner of Denny building was appropriate to meet the needs of the NSRSN program. Therefore legislators created Substitute Senate Bill 5521 to remove language related to renovation and thereby allow new construction. New language also allowed the building to be used for any activity authorized under SB 5440, removing the restriction of long-term mental health services.

By 1990, the Tsang Partnership designed a conceptual plan for a 15-bed acute care facility to be ready by July of 1992. The Office of Financial Management and DSHS rejected a proposal to add another fifteen beds for longer term care. The facility opened May 1, 1993 and operated for seventeen years. By November 1, 2010 the facility closed its doors due to state budget cuts. The operators planned to send patients to Skagit Valley Hospital, St. Joseph Medical Center in Bellingham, an evaluation and treatment center in Mukilteo or outside the region even though these facilities were frequently full. Nursing supervisor, Heather Thomas asked, "Where are they going to go? Stay in jail, or stay on the street?... I fear for our community."

The Regional Support Network Building faces Hansen Creek.
Photo: M.J. McGoffin, January 18, 2010

Appendix K: Deadline for Disposal

Washington State sought comment on the disposition of Northern State Hospital and would not release $872,000 earmarked for property improvements until a disposal plan was developed. The budget provision required that a disposal plan for transferring all or part of the property out of state ownership be available by Dec. 1, 1994.

A letter sent to Governor Mike Lowry from Don Walley, chairman of the North Cascades Multi-Service Center Advocacy Committee dated June 17, 1994, put forth his group's proposal. It called for dividing the campus into three zones. The U.S. Department of Labor would manage its Cascade Job Corp site. The State Department of Social and Health Services would provide building maintenance to several social-service programs. The third zone contained abandoned buildings that needed demolition. The proposal suggested the State remove asbestos and demolish one or two buildings each biennium using Department of Correction crews.

Mr. Walley submitted the position paper to the office of Fiscal Management. The paper represented the Skagit Council of Governments, the Economic Development Association of Skagit County, the Department of Social and Health Services, the Department of General Administration and the current tenants: Cascade Job Corps, Pioneer Center North, and the North Sound Regional Support Network. The paper reminded the state that six programs on the campus currently employed 350 people and had combined annual operating budgets in excess of $15 million. They suggested recruiting tenants such as the Washington National Guard to build a maintenance facility with an engineering battalion for flood control, regional offices for state agencies such as the Department of Fisheries, Natural Resources or Ecology. Other possibilities included long term care for aged adults, a mental health diagnostic and treatment service for children below the age of 18 years of age, or expansion of the Cascade Job Corps program.

On July 28, 1994, Peter Rell, director of the office of Job Corps in Washington D.C. requested the state transfer title of the land and buildings to the Department of Labor (DOL) in consideration of the $14,000,000 in capital improvements they had invested in the site. While the lease space was a nominal $10 per year, the utility bill amounted to $986,000 annually. They sought ownership of their own portion of the site in order to reduce their utility costs by installing their own boilers and furnaces in each building.

In the end, Job Corps agreed to remain connected to the central powerhouse heating system. The state demolished the morgue, Winfield Hall, Barkley Hall, Elliott Hall, Horton Hall, Rogers Hall and the superintendent's mansion and Moore Hall also known as the farm annex.

In 1996, the Washington National Guard built a maintenance facility east of the ponds. None of the property transferred out of state ownership.

Demolition of Winfield Building 1992. The flat roof failed around 1988 due to a plugged drain and the building collapsed.

Photo: Department of General Administration, Northern State Hospital Complex

Demolition of Elliot Building 1997.

Photo: Department of General Administration, the original Northern State Hospital complex

Appendix L: A farming legacy

In the late nineteenth century, logging companies cleared the Skagit Valley, opening up land for farming. Newly installed dikes helped contain the Skagit River and claim land for the growing agricultural industry. However, not until the Skagit River Hydroelectric Project sponsored by Seattle Light completed a series of three dams in 1949 did some measure of flood protection reach the valley farmlands.

Skagit County did not have sufficient dairy farms to supply the needs of the hospital at the turn of the twentieth century. In 1918, the farm replaced the Ayrshire cattle with Holsteins to improve milk production under the direction of herdsman, Mr. Peter Fyre. They sold Purebred bulls for profit to breeders within Skagit and adjoining counties.

In 1928, NSH began with Shropshire sheep obtained from a herder in Stanwood and later added Hampshire sheep for their wool. In addition to obtaining mutton, the men's occupational therapy department used wool in making mattresses for the hospital. Areas north of the hospital served as grazing lands for the sheep and goats. Tyee hill was alternately known as Goat Hill.

In addition to dairy cattle, the farm also raised swine, poultry, horses and mules. The swine herd represented the largest and most diverse in the county. Agricultural students from Mount Baker, Nooksack, and other Skagit and Whatcom County schools regularly visited the farm while studying the rearing of swine. In 1921, the state built the first poultry house, large enough to house 1,500 chickens. In 1944, the state constructed portable brooder houses according to Washington State College recommendations for sanitation, lighting, electric heating, and portability. This decreased disease accumulation by rotating the chickens through different areas.

Clearing land of trees, stumps and debris continued throughout the 1930s. With Hansen Creek channelized, they cultivated the low bottomlands for crops. These included strawberries, spinach, onions, lettuce, carrots, beets, pumpkin, squash, beans, cabbage, rutabagas, parsnips, bush beans, string beans, broccoli, brussel sprouts, potatoes, cauliflower, celery, chives, cucumbers, dill, endive, garlic, kohlrabi, leeks, radishes, rhubarb, peppers, parsley, turnips, alfalfa, and different feed grasses. The farm managers experimented with potato varieties and benefited from the advice of Paul Dickey, the USDA soil conservation officer who recommended crop rotations and plantings. NSH partnered with Dr. Martin Carstens, of the Northwestern Washington Experiment Station in Skagit County to try experimental seeds and obtain advice on increasing production through seed selection.

During the 1940s, with a shortage of labor throughout the agricultural community, hospital crews helped local farmers harvest their pea crops in the summers. Collaboration between the N.S.H. farm and the agricultural community laid the groundwork for a prosperous economic future in production of vegetable seeds. Today, agriculture is the No. 1 industry in Skagit County. Northern State Hospital left a legacy of excellence in husbandry and farming practices for generations of farm families in the Skagit Valley.

Skagit County Parks and Recreation contracts to have the grasses cut and bailed each summer.
Photo: M.J. McGoffin, September 10, 2009

Appendix M: Gary Williams' recommendations:

Much has happened since the closure of Northern. In 2008 Whatcom County joined other northwest counties to pass an increase in the state sales tax to raise about $2.3 million per year to treat the mentally ill and substance abuse populations. The county built a new minimum-security correctional facility, including a fifteen bed crisis triage center. To serve the mentally ill and substance abuse population 24/7. Studies proved a behavioral triage center that provided supportive care would help keep the mentally ill and substance-abusing populations out of the criminal justice system. I asked people: "Do you want to spend your tax dollars on more jails or do you want to help people get their lives back?"

One re-entry program is the Citygate Apartments in Bellingham. This program provides permanent housing for the mentally ill and substance abusers being released from jail and the State Department of Corrections. In Whatcom County we have also developed a Homeless Service Center to house the chronically mentally ill and prevent them from being evicted. The county's homeless population has been reduced by 40% in the last three years. The program costs up to $6000 a year for each patient, a fraction of what it would cost to be in the criminal justice system or inpatient hospital care.

I think we still need some of the more intensive services Northern State Hospital provided, albeit in a much smaller facility to serve as a regional intermediate care facility for some of our most challenging folks.

The regional facility would be fully integrated with the patient's home community programs and not be a "time-out" placement for exhausted local service providers.

- Continue to develop crisis triage services, mental health courts, specialized re-entry services and PACT programs (Program for Assertive Community Treatment).
- Expand the seamless continuum of community care program which relies upon a strong "no decline policy." This includes access to housing, medical care, diversion and re-entry from the criminal justice system, seamless substance abuse and mental health care and employment services.
- Expansion of the consumer oriented "Recovery" model, empowering consumers to take back as much control over their lives as possible.
- Increased reliance upon what works for folks rather than what is funded and/or what we are used to doing.
- Never forget the families and the National Alliance on Mental Illness (NAMI) who have been co-pilots on our journey.

The Regional Support Network (RSN) Executive board is made up of County elected officials from Whatcom, Skagit, Island and Snohomish counties. We have one 14-bed Evaluation and Treatment facility, three community hospital inpatient units, several large community mental health centers and linkages with an array of other community service providers.

While not yet complete, the County, RSN, and providers have increasingly embraced a holistic approach which results in successful health treatment when integrated with housing substance abuse treatment and a recovery model of client-based care.

Gary Williams' career:

- 1967-1973: Northern State Hospital
- 1973-1992: Whatcom Counseling and Psychiatric Clinic as a Community Worker, Patient Care Coordinator, Director of Emergency Services, and as Director of Case Management Services
- 1992-1998: Area Resource Coordinator for the newly formed North Sound Regional Support Network
- 1998-2008: Whatcom County Mental Health Coordinator and later as Human Services Director with the Whatcom County Health Department.

Appendix N: Skagit County Resources

The Skagit County Department of Community Services provides a wide range of programs and works with several local providers of mental health care. The department participates with the five-county North Sound Mental Health Administration (NSMHA) and receives appropriate resources through this regional body. The delivery of mental health care is constantly adapting to changes in funding sources. For the most current information, visit the websites: nsmha.org or skagitcounty.net. A few of the programs available, as of this writing, include:

- The Community Wellness Program provides short-term mental health counseling services and is funded by 0.1% county sales tax.

- The Jail Transition Program uses a post-booking case management model to facilitate safe transition from confinement to community services for inmates who have mental health disorders. The program strives to lessen recidivism and to support individuals in becoming productive members of society. NSMHA funds this program with state dollars.

- The Skagit Treatment Engagement Program, (STEP) provides outreach and engagement to individuals with mental illness who may be resistant to center-based treatment. The program connects the individuals with mental health resources, housing, and financial assistance. STEP is funded by a federal block grant until Sept 11, 2011 with funding uncertain after that date.

- The Skagit County Mental Health Court promotes public safety and reduces recidivism among offenders with mental illness through an intensive program of evaluation, treatment and frequent monitoring of compliance. Its goal is to bring stability, sobriety and safety to participants while ensuring the security and well-being of the community. The Court program draws on the expertise and cooperation of Skagit County Superior Court, Skagit County Prosecuting Attorney and Public Defender Office, public mental health providers, local advocacy and support agencies, and private providers of mental health, substance abuse and ancillary services. This is funded with 0.1% county sales tax.

- The Crisis Center in Burlington provides eleven beds to accommodate adults with mental health needs and/or substance abuse. Participants can stay up to five days. The center provides stabilization and/or detox services on a voluntary basis. A discharge plan may link a participant with further treatment. Some participants go directly to inpatient chemical dependency treatment. The center is supported by a combination of local alcohol sales tax, 0.1% county sales tax, and NSMHA state funds.

- The At-Risk Intervention Specialist (ARIS) program serves students ages pre-school to eighteen. ARIS began in 1991 as a cooperative venture between Skagit County government and the seven local school districts. The length of service is typically between 12--18 months. Funds come from a Readiness to Learn Grant and county general funds.

Endnotes

Essay #5, pages 24-25. Data obtained from Dr. Doughty's biennial reports at the Washington State Archives office at Western Washington University.

Essay #6, pages 29-30. A copy of Dr. McLeish's biennial report for 1910-1912 obtained from the North Cascades Gateway Center.

Essay #7, pages 31-32. The Skagit County Historical Museum in LaConner, Washington had several boxes of Northern State Hospital newsletters.

Dick Fallis included Eric's story in his book, Amid Fields of Alyssum: A YEAR AT NORTHERN STATE, published in 1984 by Skagit Advocate Publishing Company. We are not told Eric's diagnosis.

Essay #8, pages 44-45. Date obtained from: "Controversial Psychosurgery Resulted in a Nobel Prize." Nobelprize.org. 24 Jul 2010 http://nobelprize.org/nobel_prizes/medicine/laureates/1949/moniz-article.html

Essay #12, pages 46-47. The matron's report was filed among Dr. Doughty's paperwork at the Washington State Archives office at Western Washington University.

Essay #26, page 95. The Skagit Valley Herald published a twelve part series entitled: "A New Road to Mental Health" by staff reporters Nancy Erickson and Noel Johnson.

Appendix C: *History of the Cascade Job Corps Program*, pages 123-126. Data obtained from the Skagit Regional Overall Economic Development Plan, June, 1975 page 9.

Interview with Bill Shuler, April 28, 2010, Sedro-Woolley, Washington.

Appendix D: PORTAL, pages 128-130. Data obtained from: the Washington State Department of Social and Health Services, Mental Health Division brochure, the Northern State Advocacy Committee, and the Skagit Valley Herald article: "Budget cuts target S-W facility" February 4, 1993.

Appendix E: Ten proposals, pages 132-134. In 1986, the Legislature adopted a measure at the request of Skagit County to direct the Department of Natural Resources (DNR) to lease at least 250 acres of Northern State property as a potential site for the Skagit County Fairgrounds (RCW36.37.160.) In 1990, the Legislature directed the DNR to sell 750 acres to Skagit County. The county purchased the land in 1991 for $833,000.

Appendix F: The Norlum Foundation, pages 134-136. The Norlum Foundation self-published their by-laws on June 28, 1984. The foundation's primary objective was to "create and found a charitable, health, and education, not-for-profit foundation for the sole benefit of programs operating at or in conjunction with the Northern State Multiple Service Center, Sedro-Woolley, Washington, to assist, strengthen and further in every proper and useful way the purposes, work and services of the programs, to develop, enhance and utilize the ties of interest, concern and affections existing between the programs and their friends throughout the state and nation.

Appendix G: Neurological center pilot project, page 137. Senate Bill No. 4914 allocated $30,000 for the neurological center pilot project. Northern State Neurological Center Pilot Project report, Northern State Campus, Sedro-Woolley, Washington, published by SCOG.

Appendix I: *A Blueprint*, pages 140-141. The Senate approved a $100,000 appropriation to develop a long-range plan for the use of the Northern State Hospital facility to be submitted to the office of Financial Management and the Legislature by January 8, 1990. General Administration delivered the Blueprint for the Northern State Multi-Purpose Center in 1991 and requested more time to investigate further options.

Appendix J: The Regional Support Network, page 141-143. Data obtained from the *Skagit Valley Herald* October 8, 1988 (the article title was missing from the newspaper clipping.)

The *Skagit Valley Herald* article: "Mental health plan carried big price tag." November 15, 1989. The Blueprint for Northern State Multi-Purpose Center.

The *Skagit Valley Herald* article: "Budget cuts force mental treatment facility in S-W to close." October 20, 2010.

Appendix K: Deadline for disposal. Pages 144-145. Data obtained from the *Skagit Valley Herald*, May 2, 1994

Draft Disposition of the North Cascade Multi-Service Center: Position paper June 1994.

Letter to Governor Lowry from Peter Rell, U.S. Department of Labor, July 28, 1994.

Appendix L: A farming legacy, pages 148-149. Data obtained from Artifacts Consulting Inc. "Cultural Resource Assessment," Northern State Hospital, 2008.

Skagit.wsu.edu, 17 December 2009.

Closing Remarks

Across the breakfast table from my husband one morning, I began telling him how doctors performed lobotomies. He had just sat down to his freshly brewed Sumatra coffee, six ounces of pulp-free orange juice and half a whole-wheat bagel with crunchy peanut butter. Then he stopped, took off his glasses and tipped his face into his hands. In my clinical coldness, I had looked at lobotomies with the emotional distance of a surgical nurse but my husband did not have this background to protect him.

"I feel their pain," he said. And he meant right then and there. Past and present blended into one dimension of time. This is the kind of compassion our human spirit is capable of. Evolution may determine our physical characteristics but civilization will determine our advancement of humanity. Evolution passes on genes: Humanity passes on stories. And stories enliven our capacity for compassion.

I am passing on stories to the reader and to future generations. Every so often, an archaeological dig reveals some breaking news and we react as though some long-lost relative has been discovered, some clue about who we are. We need not look so far afield.

We who feel the transience of our fleeting lives are drawn to Northern State Hospital's weighty presence. We watch with mis-giving as historic buildings are torn down or when the earth is harmed, aware that somehow this leaves us dis-franchised. Let us preserve our past, not just the built environment, but also the earth's integrity and all the human stories that spring from the soil of living here, stories of in-spiration, *in+ spirare*, to breathe, to infuse life into.